Food: FACTS, FOIBLES, AND FABLES

THE ORIGINS OF HUMAN NUTRITION

Also by A. T. W. Simeons, M.D.

MAN'S PRESUMPTUOUS BRAIN

A. T. W. *Simeons*, M.D.

Food:

FACTS,

FOIBLES,

FABLES

THE ORIGINS OF HUMAN NUTRITION

Funk & Wagnalls, New York

Contents

Science should not ask: Is this true?, but rather:
Is this reasonable and can it be argued?
                    —SIR JAMES JEANS

Foreword and Forewarning

THIS BOOK is written for interested laymen like myself. I am a physician, not a biologist, paleontologist, anthropologist, or behaviorist, though I do browse—alas, all too leisurely—through a small fraction of the scientific literature dealing with these burgeoning offshoots the ageless art of healing. Being thus poorly qualified, it is inevitable that my book is a blend of facts and fantasies, of musings, mullings and meditations based on what to the expert must appear to be very scrappy knowledge.

Perhaps it is a sort of science fiction, except that instead of looking into a weird and terrifying future it looks back into a hardly less weird and terrifying past. We all know that the science fiction of today is peculiarly apt to become the science of tomorrow. My apology is, therefore, that the same may prove to be true of an unhampered discussion of some aspects of our evolutionary past. The more we try to unravel the complexities of evolution the more we find ourselves surrounded by as yet unfathomable lacunae.

I cannot always let the reader know what is science and

what is fiction or speculation; often because I myself do not know just where to draw that line. If the reader is sufficiently curious and interested he will have to find that out for himself from the latest writings of specialists. It would, I feel, be a pity to roughen the flow of a scientifically flavored narrative with encumbrances which would here amount to scientific pedantry.

Herewith the professionals have had their warning, and unless they enjoy gunning for inquisitive trespassers on their respective fields they should not read on. If on the other hand the layman enjoys a glimpse into our still very mysterious past, he will have rewarded this scientifically naughty enterprise.

Food: FACTS, FOIBLES, AND FABLES

THE ORIGINS OF HUMAN NUTRITION

On Feeding in General

WE ARE accustomed to distinguish animals that eat other animals, those that eat plants and those that regularly eat both. Thus we speak of carnivores, herbivores and omnivores. These distinctions, however, are not nearly as clear cut as they seem, and as they will continually recur in our discussion we must have a very precise understanding of the extent to which they are valid.

THE CARNIVORES

The term "carnivorous" literally means flesh-eating, but it is convenient to include the milk-drinking young of

all mammals, and animals that live exclusively on insects—
the insectivores—under this main heading.

It is perhaps worth noting that all animals are born
carnivorous, provided the term is used in this wide sense.
The fertilized egg cell and the growing embryo, regardless
of whether it grows inside an exposed shell or in its
mother's womb, obtains all the nourishment it requires
before it hatches or is born from its mother's body. As this
is also the case with those lowly spineless animals that
multiply by budding, the carnivorous beginning of life
applies to the whole animal kingdom.

There are two kinds of true flesh eaters: those that
hunt and kill their prey—the predators; and those that eat
the flesh of animals that have died or have been killed by
the predators—the scavengers or carrion eaters. Among terrestrial animals the most typical representatives of the
predators are the members of the large family of the cats:
the lions, tigers, panthers, pumas, jaguars, the domestic
cats, and their numerous kin. Of course there are many
other predators, but they are not quite as highly specialized in their adaptations to predacious feeding.

All cats have tearing fangs, cutting molars and sharp
claws which they can retract. They do not hunt in packs
like wolves and dogs, and their intestinal tract is short, fast-
working and highly efficient. They gorge themselves at
their kill and can then go one or more days without food.
Yet even such apparently exclusive carnivora as the cats
cannot survive healthily on flesh alone.

A rich friend of mine, a Parsee merchant of Bombay,
owned a large zoo, and one day I rode in a dazzling motor
launch across the Bombay harbor to Uran to see his animals. The zoo was superbly kept by a host of attendants in
a lush old tropical garden. I found the animals in excellent
condition except for the large cats which looked scruffy,
listless, and undernourished. Their keepers and my friend

assured me that they got the choicest cuts of meat and as much as they would eat of horseflesh, goats, etc. The butcher of the zoo confirmed this and stated that the offal of the animals slaughtered was given to the wolves, jackals, and birds of prey, all of which seemed to be in perfect health.

Knowing from travels in Africa and from observations in India that most wild cats start their feast by devouring the entrails of their prey, I suggested an experiment. We gave the lions, tigers, and panthers the unwashed entrails of freshly slaughtered goats, and these they ate ravenously. It was then decided that henceforth all large cats should be given entrails full of half-digested vegetable matter together with their meat and bones. Two months later I revisited the zoo. The change for the better in the cats was dramatic and enthusiastically admitted by their keepers. Thus even such typical flesh eaters as cats require some vegetable matter to remain healthy and this they obtain from the intestines of their prey.

We know that when a cat or an owl catches a mouse or a bird, it eats it whole with its vegetable-containing intestine. I have visited dozens of zoos in many parts of the world and make a point of going there alone to spend more time in friendly chats with the keepers than in watching the animals. It is astonishing how much one can learn from these dedicated men. For instance, I have been assured that when in spring grass grows high outside an open lion cage the animals will reach through the bars with their paws to draw in and eat tufts of grass.

Bears are classified as carnivora, but we all know of their predeliction for honey; also, they will readily eat fruit and, in captivity, buns, bananas, peanuts and carrots. Dogs are carnivorous; yet every fancier knows that his pets will not thrive on meat alone and that he must add some vegetable matter to their feeds. The huge, shaggy white dogs of the shepherds in the Abruzzi Mountains look much like the sheep they tend and are fed mostly on spaghetti, polenta made from maize, and rice with olive oil. Only in the lambing season do the dogs get the afterbirths, the still-births, and the lambs that die after birth. It has also been observed that wolves in the wild eat grass just as dogs sometimes do. Thus we see that carnivores are only predominantly flesh-eating and not exclusively so.

Leopards have a particular hankering for dogs, which are themselves carnivorous, but as a general rule flesh-eaters feed on herbivora. The large amount of half-digested vegetable matter which their intestines contain may be a strong motive for this preference.

Nor do the scavengers or carrion eaters live on flesh alone. Often they, too, can be seen dragging away the filled entrails of dead animals, and they have a further nutritional advantage in that the rapidly rotting meat they live on is teeming with bacteria and molds. These the powerful digestive juices of the scavengers rapidly kill, but the mass of the bodies of these microorganisms, rich in proteins, vitamins, and minerals, are certainly of great nutritional importance to such animals, particularly as bacteria and molds are closer to the vegetable than to the animal kingdom.

THE INSECTIVORES

As insects belong to the animal kingdom, animals that feed on them are, broadly speaking, carnivores, although they represent a specialized group. Yet, here again, they are not exclusive meat-eaters because their diet is rounded out by the vegetable content of the intestines of their prey, which almost certainly represents an essential dietary supplement of considerable nutritional importance. Incidentally, the term *insectivorous* is zoologically not quite accurate, as most insectivores—apart from some highly specialized forms such as, for instance, the anteaters—also feed on spiders and worms, which are not insects.

Mammals that feed on insects are usually small, such as bats, moles, hedgehogs, tree shrews, and many others. Except for mature caterpillars or the fat larvae and eggs of beetles and bees, insects—particularly the flying ones—have little caloric value compared with their bulk. This means that warm-blooded insectivores, whether mammals or birds, must devour an enormous number of insects to cover their daily nutritional requirements. The chase may also call for a very high energy output, and this must be provided for in the diet. Hedgehogs, moles or swallows, for instance, must eat about their own weight in worms and insects daily to stay fit, to reproduce, and—in the case of the hedgehog and the mole—to suckle their young.

Thus, the living conditions, or ecology, of insectivorous, warm-blooded animals are very harsh and exacting. As we shall see in the next chapter, this may be the reason why they have retained their small size, why they have survived many millions of years without suffering extinction in spite of their rather primitive stage of evolution, and why they have very rarely, if ever, given rise to a wide variety of new species. We shall also see later that the apparent exception to this rule, the insectivorous tree shrew, believed to have been the starting point of the whole populous family of the primates which includes man, may need a somewhat different interpretation.

There are, however, a few exceptions to the prevailing rule that insectivores are small in size. These exceptions include anteaters such as the African aardvark, the South

American anteaters, and the Old World pangolins. These species differ from other insectivores in that they feed exclusively on ants and termites and have highly developed feeding specializations such as a long sticky tongue, powerful digging forelimbs, and an almost complete absence of teeth. These various anteaters are not otherwise related to each other, but their evolution towards an ever better adaptation to their mode of living has run parallel. There exists, for instance, a small, rat-like Australian marsupial, the numbat, which feeds on termites. It too has developed digging claws and a long sticky tongue, though it has not given up its teeth; in fact, with 52 teeth it has more than any other marsupial.

According to a personal communication from Prof. R. Hoffstetter of the Parisian National Museum of Natural History, who is one of the greatest authorities on the subject, the aardvark descended from long-extinct herbivorous mammals, the *condylartheres,* which lived in the Miocene some 25 million years ago. Much earlier, possibly 200 million years ago the South American anteaters derived from toothless, poorly specialized insectivorous Mesozoic ancestors that were rather close to the most primitive surviving mammals, the egg-laying duck-billed platypus and the spiny anteater of Australia. The pangolins on the other hand, evolved out of more advanced insectivores which already had teeth and lived in the Eocene-Oligocene about 50 million years ago. The pangolins subsequently lost their teeth when they specialized in ant-eating. This strange parallelism among species that are in no way related to each other is a common phenomenon in evolution and is known as concurrence.

In these particular cases we are dealing with species that have remained essentially unchanged throughout many millions of years and that have not, to our knowledge, given rise to new forms. Yet they could retain a relatively large body size because of their ability to break into hard termite hills and to collect vast numbers of insects on their long, sticky tongues, which they dart in and out of the nests. Other insectivorous animals that must chase or search for their prey cannot feed so abundantly with such relative leisure. However, all large insectivores, such as the armadillo, are tropical and often burrowing animals which require less food for the maintenance of their body temperature than animals living in colder climates.

For the purpose of further discussion it is important to remember that insectivores are generally small, that they are extremely conservative in an evolutionary sense, and that they appear to survive as species for incredibly long periods of time once they are fully adapted to their mode of life. Compared with them, herbivorous mammals are relative newcomers, and all surviving carnivorous mammals are almost upstarts.

It may seem a little farfetched to discuss insectivores in a book on human feeding; but we must remember that in many parts of the world fat grubs, fried ants, locusts and bee larvae are even now considered delicacies and perfectly legitimate items of the human diet. Nearly all Primates, the order to which man belongs, are predominantly frugivorous; but apart from fruit, they relish insects as a snack. Moreover, the primates take their origin from an insectivorous tree-shrew-like animal. Thus, insects have played a most important role in the evolution of human feeding and many relics of an insectivorous past are still evident in man today.

THE HERBIVORES

It has been pointed out that no animal is herbivorous from the beginning of its existence. In carnivorous animals the gut undergoes hardly any significant changes from birth to maturity and never deviates very far from the original primitive vertebrate pattern. In herbivores, on the other hand, far-reaching changes in the anatomical structure and in the physiology—secretions, mechanics and bacterial flora—are required to make vegetable matter wholly assimilable and nutritious. We need but think of the mechanical complexities involved in ruminant digestion with its need for chewing the cud.

In mammals the ability to live on vegetable matter is a fairly recent and high evolutionary achievement; particularly as most reptilian forms out of which the mammals evolved some 300 million years ago in the trees of the Carboniferous age were almost certainly insectivorous. Though flesh-eating and herbivorous reptiles did at that time live on the ground, it is hard to believe that they could have survived in the Carboniferous tree tops, a drastic change of habitat. There may have been a few other reptiles in those trees, but there were as yet no birds, so that it seems highly improbable that a flesh eater could survive there.

As for the herbivores, they have a way of specializing rather rapidly. At that time their choice of vegetable food was limited; flowering plants and the grasses had not yet evolved. It is therefore equally difficult to imagine that herbivorous reptiles adapted to feeding on the ground could survive in the towering crowns of the Carboniferous forests that covered most of the land. Insects, however, were already diversifed and abundant both on the ground and in the trees. It would seem then that insectivores had the best chance of survival and probably did survive to give rise to all the mammals, of which the most primitive—the already mentioned platypus and spiny anteater—are to this day insectivorous.

Herbivora can be divided into a number of categories according to their feeding habits. There are browsers that live on leaves, grazers that feed on grasses, the frugivora live on fruit, nut eaters, and others. The herbivora may also be divided according to their position in the systematic classification of animals into hooved animals, rodents, primates, etc. What is important is that a change-over from carnivorous or insectivorous to herbivorous feeding, with almost certainly an omnivorous transitory phase, is a staggering evolutionary achievement and must have had a profound influence on the course of evolution both as regards the finer adaptation of existing trends and the creation of entirely new genera.

Just as the carnivores are not exclusively carnivorous, because they also eat a certain amount of food of vegetable origin, so the herbivora also eat and probably need a carnivorous supplement. On a lush meadow, on leaves and bark of trees and shrubs, and in ripe and overripe fruit there is a surprisingly large amount of animal—chiefly insect—life. All these insects, caterpillars, grubs, and eggs are eaten by the herbivores in the course of their normal feeding. A monkey relishes with obvious delight a fat grub which it finds in its fruit, and it is generally recognized that domestic or confined herbivora will thrive only if given extra vitamins, minerals and proteins of animal origin in addition to their staple food. They do not require such supplements in the wild because the animal food which they unwittingly ingest—when they graze or browse or eat fruit in their normal habitat—supplies this need.

THE OMNIVORES

From what has gone before it becomes clear that all adult mammals are, very strictly speaking, omnivorous. The carnivores require some dietary supplement of vegetable origin and the herbivores a supplement of animal origin. Yet there exists a need for a third category to include those animals that actively search for food from both the animal and vegetable kingdoms in roughly equal quantities and without any very marked preference.

Quite apart from its dental equipment a horse would probably suffer indigestion and die if fed exclusively on steaks, just as would a tiger compelled to eat raw carrots only. The tiger's digestive tract can cope comfortably with the predigested vegetable matter in the intestines of its prey and even with small quantities of raw—and somewhat larger quantities of boiled—vegetable food. Similarly, a cow can digest insects that are well crushed, as well as bone or fish meal. But none of these animals or their relations will go deliberately in search of such atypical food, whereas the omnivorous animal will do just this.

All omnivorous animals have a structurally and physiologically primitive gut, in the sense that it is not far removed from the early vertebrate pattern. Their teeth, their stomach, their appendix, and their colon are halfway between these organs as found in true carnivores and in true herbivores; the latter having the larger dimensions in all these respects.

Of course it is possible that modern omnivora are in a transitory phase in which it is difficult to say whether they are heading in a carnivorous or a herbivorous direction. This will to a large extent depend on prevailing ecological conditions. As long as animal food is plentiful and can be collected without excessive exposure to predators, the tendency towards carnivorous feeding will increase. A shortage of animal food or increasing danger from predators will favor the herbivorous trend.

This dependence on prevailing ecological conditions is also evident in modern man. The Eskimo is predominantly carnivorous, because in his ecological niche meat is more plentiful than cereals. In India, rice is cheaper than meat and can be indefinitely preserved, while meat rots in a day; so we have strict vegetarians among the higher castes. The Brahmins have gone so far as to make a religious tenet out of the avoidance of animal food and will eat neither meat nor fish nor fowl nor eggs; and the Jains even guard against inadvertently swallowing insects by covering their mouths. But since omnivorous man (and, as we have seen, even the herbivores) cannot live exclusively on vegetable matter, the vegetarians make up for the need for food of animal origin by drinking large quantities of milk.

A MATTER OF TEETH

It is only under the rarest circumstances that the whole body of an extinct species is found preserved intact. An example is the case of the woolly mammoths found in

Siberian ice. Preserved in this deep-freeze even the animal's last meal could be reconstructed from the contents of its stomach some hundreds of thousands of years after it died. In general, however, paleontologists have only one source of direct evidence of what an extinct species ate; and that is its coprolites, which are fossilized excrement. Their careful microscopic examination can be surprisingly rewarding, as such fine structures as pollen may be identifiably preserved. Obviously, it must first be established to which species the coprolite belongs; but, fortunately, droppings of each species are highly characteristic, and an expert can usually identify them almost as easily as a fragment of fossil bone, particularly if he can date the strata in which the coprolite was found.

When coprolites are not available, the paleontologist must depend on his knowledge of the climate, the geophysical conditions, and the fauna and the flora prevailing at the time when the species lived in order to know what it might have eaten and what it could not have eaten. Finally he can, by analogy, arrive at certain conclusions by examining the fossil teeth of the species, but he can know nothing of the animals' intestinal organization.

In practice, the study of teeth is by far the most commonly applied procedure. Teeth, the hardest tissue a vertebrate can produce, are the most likely part of the body to be preserved. There can be little objection to this method as a means of grossly differentiating carnivores from herbivores. On dental evidence alone no one would suspect an elephant or a horse of being carnivorous, because their teeth have a grinding surface which is gradually worn down in a way that eating flesh would never do.

Yet we must be careful and remember that the walrus which feeds on mollusks and is therefore carnivorous also has grinding teeth. If the walrus had become extinct and our only evidence of its existence were such a grinder, we would almost certainly conclude that the animal to which this tooth belonged was herbivorous. The bears have teeth that are typically carnivorous, but only the polar bear has remained completely flesh-eating. In most other bears a substantial part of their nutrition is supplied by the vegetable kingdom, so that when classified by their feeding habits only, they should be called omnivores. If our only evidence of the existence of baboons were the large canines of an old male, we would have little hesitation in assuming that the animal to whom these teeth belonged was carnivorous. While it is true that hungry baboons will occasionally kill and devour lambs and other animals, they cannot be described as being carnivorous.

Finally, let us take the case of modern man—say an Eskimo—and let us assume that in some distant future *Homo sapiens* has become extinct and that he has been replaced by *Homo supersapiens*. Now if a superpaleontologist should one day discover the fossil jaw of our Eskimo, he would, in the absence of all other evidence, almost certainly conclude that the jaw belonged to an animal that was herbivorous; and if he knew of the climatic conditions under which the Eskimo lived, the problem of how he got his greens would sorely vex our superscientist.

As we shall see later, this whole question of carnivorous versus herbivorous feeding becomes extremely important when we deal with man's earliest ancestors, so we must remember not to be led astray by excessive dogmatism in the matter of teeth.

In this chapter we have sorted out some of the terminology and some of the basic concepts which will be continually recurring in what is to follow. We must now discuss the possible role that nutritional factors may have played in shaping our evolution.

T W O

Feeding and Evolution

IF WE glance through a wide-angle lens at our vast knowl-edge of animal evolution through hundreds of millions of years, perhaps the most striking feature of this grandiose process is that it seems so highly erratic. Yet when we look closer into the history of individual species, we usually see a continuous progress towards higher specialization and better adaptation to prevailing ecological conditions, at least from the specific animal's point of view. Yet such evolutionary changes may for no immediately apparent reason proceed with incredible rapidity or seem almost at a standstill.

When an already highly differentiated animal—for in-stance, the ancestor of a tapeworm—takes to parasitic life, most of its organs such as its mouth, its means of loco-motion, its defenses against enemies, and its external re-productive organs become useless and gradually disappear; the body turns into a chain of almost inert sacks filled with ovaries having a fantastic capacity. To us this will appear to be a process of degeneration, while from the tapeworm's point of view it is a marvelous and progressive adaptation to its peculiar living conditions.

Perhaps the only negative aspect of the process of evolution is that certain adaptations, once initiated, appear to go beyond the point of usefulness and so become an impediment rather than an asset. Certain early brachiopods —double-shelled marine animals superficially resembling clams—developed a double horn-like structure over the hinge of their shells. As the brachiopod grew older the horns became larger, until their tips met, making it impossible for the animal to open its shell for feeding and thus causing its death. It is reasonable to believe that with an ever more precocious development of these horns a point was reached when the shells locked before reproductive maturity was achieved, and that this may have contributed to the rather sudden extinction of these once wildly prosperous species.

Among the ruling reptiles—the dinosaurs—some forms specialized in such enormous bodies that they could eventually only live and move half-submerged in water which buoyed them. Gradually they were deprived of the terrestrial food to which they were adjusted, and this may well have caused their extinction. Though our hippopotamus, a member of the pig family, is still fairly agile on land, it is conceivable that it is heading in the same direction. In another pig, the Babirussa, the tusks, instead of curling outward, grow straight up from the upper jaw, pierce the noselike horns, and then as the animal grows older start curving back in a spiral in front of the eyes, which changes them from a useful weapon into a useless impediment.

It is hard to imagine what purpose could have been served by the huge back-curling tusks of an old male woolly mammoth. In young animals the tusks grew

straight downward and may have been used as weapons or
for raking up the snow and ice that covered the tundra
when the animal was in search of food. The curling tusks
of older mammoths would seem to be quite useless for
either purpose and, in fact, a hindrance. It is plausible that
this freakish development of the tusks contributed to the
downfall of the species.

THE PATTERNS OF EVOLUTION

Apart from such seemingly senseless trends contrary to
the best interests of the species, we can discern three rather
distinct evolutionary patterns.

The first is what we may describe as *conservation*. A
species, genus or order continues to survive almost un-
altered for tens and sometimes hundreds of millions of
years. Such very old species never seem to give rise to
radically new forms. It is as if the price they pay for long
immunity to extinction is evolutionary sterility.

Among the invertebrates, the oyster is one typical
example of this pattern. In their early career, almost 600
million years ago, the oysters appear to have given rise to
some offshoots such as the *Gryphaea* and the *Exogyra,* but
since then they are not known to have produced any viable
side-branches. Among vertebrates, a few survivors of the
ruling reptiles such as the turtle, the tortoise, the croco-
diles and the marine iguanas of the Galapagos Archipelago
are examples of the pattern of conservation; and among
mammals, the platypus and the spiny anteater are perhaps
the most outstanding. Though much more dramatic examples of this pattern can be found among invertebrates,

we will for the sake of familiarity say that conservation is a pattern of the "platypus" type.

The second pattern, which we will call *specialization,* differs radically from conservation. It may be compared to a clipped hedge. From a stem-form new side-shoots are continually emerging, and these again branch into side-shoots of their own. However, as in a clipped hedge, these side-shoots cannot all continue to develop. There always comes a point at which either the main stem or the branch becomes extinct. Sometimes the branch takes over further evolution, in which case the main stem becomes extinct; or the branch dies out and the main stem continues to give rise to new branchings.

A typical example of this evolutionary pattern among mammals is the horse. As far as we know, it all started about 60 million years ago in the early Eocene with an animal about the size of a fox terrier, Eohippus or Dawn-horse, known to science as *Hyracotherium.* During the passage of millions of years this little creature gave rise to hundreds of side-branches of bewildering complexity, until finally *Equus,* our modern horse, evolved as the sole survivor out of a vast number of trial runs of which we have astoundingly rich fossil evidence. Each surviving form was a little better adjusted to prevailing ecological conditions than its predecessors, particularly in the early Miocene, about 25 million years ago, when the grasses spread over the earth and some forms of early horses switched from browsing on the leaves of shrubs and trees to grazing exclusively on what grew on the ground as grass. The grazers continued to flourish, while all the browsers died out.

It is probable that the earliest horse, *Hyracotherium,* is ancestral to some other herbivorous forms, but from then on the family tree of the horses never produced anything other than better horses.

Examples of the *specialization* pattern can be found in

any phylum, and it may be taken for granted that all species must first go through a phase of specialization before they can, in a few surviving forms, enter into the "platypus" type of conservation. However, as the horse is perhaps the best documented example of this pattern, and in order to stay within the class of mammals, we will say that specialization is of the "horse" type.

Finally, there is a third and rather mysterious evolutionary pattern which we will call *diversification*, though in scientific writing it is often referred to as *radiation*, a term which to me seems rather too metaphorical. Diversification again differs radically from the other patterns in that it is almost explosive in character. In an incredibly short span of time, geologically speaking, there appears on the scene of life a large variety of entirely new species, genera and families which continue to branch into new forms with relatively little evidence of extinction.

Characteristic of this pattern of diversification is the almost constant phenomenon of "missing links." The new forms seem to appear suddenly from nowhere. The only possible explanation for the apparent absence of "links" is that the form that gave rise to the diversification in the first instance becomes extinct as soon as the new forms are established. Contrary to the "platypus" type of conservation, extinction is the price paid for evolutionary fertility.

There are many examples of this pattern of diversification. Perhaps the most dramatic occurred about 600 million years ago in pre-Cambrian oceans. These seas certainly contained some very primitive forms of life of which hardly any traces remain. Then quite suddenly, in the early Cambrian period, the waters began to swarm with entirely new forms of life—highly organized animals belonging to more than five hundred different species in seven phyla that have left fossil traces of their existence.

We have no idea how these already highly developed

forms of life originated or who their ancestors were. In full possession of all their respective characteristics, there appear in quite fantastic numbers trilobites which led to the crustaceans, spiders and insects, highly diversified brachiopods, sponges, coelenterates, mollusks, worms and echinoderms. Though we know that this cannot be so, these forms appear paleontologically as if created ready-made.

Among vertebrates the fossil record shows the astoundingly rich diversification which occurred in the ruling reptiles. In hundreds of species they conquered the land, returned to an aquatic life which their ancestors, the amphibians, had only recently abandoned, and there established their undisputed dominance. They also produced flying forms of gigantic size which ruled the air.

When the first mammals descended from the trees, they rapidly grew in size and split up into a vast diversity of herbivores and carnivores, of hunters and hunted. Similarly explosive diversifications took place when among the plants the angiosperms and later the grasses evolved. Among insects numerous explosive diversifications could be cited. The birds diversified spectacularly once they had shed their last reptilian characteristics. In mammals the most recent wide diversification occurred when a tiny tree shrew gave rise to the vast and populous order of the Primates to which we belong, and which we will take as typifying this third evolutionary pattern.

Thus we distinguish:

1) The pattern of conservation or "platypus" type
2) The pattern of specialization or "horse" type
3) The pattern of diversification or "primate" type

More About Evolutionary Patterns

It might be argued that these patterns do not really exist, but that they are merely the result of our sketchy paleontological record. In answer, it can be said that the roots and edges of these patterns have been most diligently studied and that this search has hitherto been in vain. Paleontologists have spent a lifetime studying pre-Cambrian rocks for evidence of the ancestors of Cambrian phyla; the rocks are empty and almost void of anything larger than microscopic life in the strata that have been studied. In spite of our huge collections of early reptilian fossils, we still have only the haziest idea of how their staggering diversification took place. On the other hand, most careful searching has never turned up essentially different forms that could have originated from species that reached the pattern of conservation such as oysters, turtles, the platypus or the spiny anteater.

Perhaps many of us are still more conditioned to Darwinian thinking than we realize. Darwin knew nothing of the nature of mutations and the modern science of genetics. He saw evolution as a struggle for life and a survival of the fittest. Following his train of thought, we are still appalled by the harsh cruelty of the evolutionary process with millions of once-thriving species being forced to give up the struggle in irrevocable extinction. This ghastly spectacle has so dominated our thinking that we have been rather apt to overlook or gloss over the fact that many species have for untold eons comfortably survived all ecological onslaughts and outlived every threat of extinction.

On the other hand, perhaps we do not fully appreciate the fantastic exuberance of diversification in which the struggle for survival seems strangely abated. What Darwin saw and described was the pattern of specialization, to which his theory still largely applies. For the other two patterns it may need some modification.

In Darwin's sense there is a continuous moderate degree of ecological pressure, not harsh enough to prevent trial runs with some mutations for a considerable span of time, but too harsh to permit a luxuriant viable diversification. He saw ecological pressure as more or less constant during the ages. Yet it seems much more probable that ecological variations fluctuate widely. We may have conditions of extreme harshness in which any species that had once fully adapted itself to such conditions would be able to survive, but not to give rise to new forms. Under such stringency the slightest mutational deviation from the fully adapted stem-form would not have been viable. Here, then, we have the pattern of conservation of the "platypus" type.

The other extreme is widest ecological latitude with little or no struggle for survival owing to a superabundance of food, freedom from predators, parasites, etc. Under such conditions the species will not only thrive numerically and therefore increase the number of mutations occurring, but a few of these mutations will be viable though diverging in some respects from the stem-form. When a certain number of mutations are able to survive, they become the starting point of new species which, having had the initial chance of establishing themselves, can then assume a specializing, "horse" type of evolutionary pattern. They finally become so highly specialized that those who survive the process of specialization eventually come to live a conservation type of existence. Thus, at a given moment, species that are following any of the three patterns are living side by side.

By far the largest number of species of which fossil

evidence reaches us never took part in the process of diversification and therefore never gave rise to new phyla or orders. They are the product of the "horse" type pattern; they flourish for a certain period and then die out. To use a botanical metaphor, they are branches, not new independent plants like those that grow from the runners of a strawberry and, with rapid withering of the connecting runner, become completely independent new plants. This is what appears to happen in diversification.

DEGREES OF ECOLOGICAL PRESSURE

At this point the reader may well ask what all this has to do with the origins of human nutrition. I ask his forbearance as now matters of feeding re-enter the picture.

Hitherto we have been generally speaking of degrees of ecological pressure; now we must consider what determines this degree of pressure. Many factors are involved— climate, geological conditions, the flora, and the presence of predators (or, in their case, the scarcity or abundance of prey).

The life of insectivorous mammals is, as we have seen, extremely strenuous and demanding; their ecology is harsh. When the early carnivores spread over the earth, the contemporary herbivores had not yet had time to develop the speed which went with long legs, nor the defensive organization of the herd, and they had neither hooves nor horns. Moreover, they were slow-witted. For the carnivores this was an Eldorado of superabundance available with a minimum of effort. They enjoyed a wide ecological latitude, with ease and security and the chance to diversify rapidly into new and larger species. The fossil record shows that they made fullest use of this evolutionary opportunity.

We can imagine that a sudden rise in the temperature of the pre-Cambrian seas brought on by the end of the pre-Cambrian Ice Age, or a change in the mineral content of the water, due perhaps to submarine volcanic eruptions, led to an explosive increase in plankton which suddenly furnished an inexhaustible supply of food for any form of life that could subsist on it. Such few earliest forms as were already present probably increased in the number of individuals which in turn led to a large genetic pool from which many mutations could arise. Some of these mutations proved viable in such wide ecological latitude. Where there was nothing to decimate their offspring, their numbers multiplied into trillions within an incredibly short time, and so for us there appears a picture of explosive evolution in the fossil record. Today we are shocked by the population explosion we are witnessing during our lifetime in our own species as a result of diminishing ecological pressure, at least as far as warfare and epidemic diseases are concerned; but how very limited is the number of our progeny compared with the fantastic fertility of those early invertebrates.

When the first reptiles evolved out of water-bound amphibians and were for the first time able to roam and breed on virgin land far away from oceans, rivers, and lakes, the earth was covered with plants and they had no enemies of any kind. A large number of mutations could establish a new ecological niche for themselves and thrive in a spate of diversification. We know that the mutation of a single gene can bring about far-reaching changes in many parts of the body. Where large numbers of individuals are concerned mutations will be more frequent; if there occurs some change which is of advantage to the mutated form and, particularly, if several such mutated forms find each other in a new ecological niche, a subspecies may be born in a single generation. If then this fresh genetic pool becomes geographically or ecologically isolated from the stem-form, it will rapidly evolve into a new species, losing many of the characteristics of the form from which it originated, and within a few more generations it may become difficult to say where the new species came from.

A modern example of how rapidly evolutionary changes can take place is furnished by the so-called *industrial melanism* of moths observed during the last hundred years in England and Western Europe. Long before industrialization some species of moths had developed light-colored, speckled wings which closely resembled the color of the bark of the trees on which they rested during the day; this effectively protected them from being spotted by the birds that preyed on them. But as these trees became grimy and sooty from the smoking factory chimneys, these moths became more and more conspicuous and might have disappeared altogether had not happy gene mutations produced new black varieties. In what in evolutionary terms is an incredibly short time the black mutations with the right protective coloring continued to multiply and have now almost replaced the lighter varieties of a number of species. If the tree trunks had become black overnight instead of in the course of a hundred years, if the moth-eating birds had been very numerous and if the mutations had occurred just at the right moment, the process would have been still further speeded up; it might have occurred in a few generations, and all trace of the light-colored variety might have disappeared in an equally short time.

The birds descended from reptiles, but not as one might think from the flying pterodactyls. Their ancestors must have gone through a long and grueling struggle before they shed their reptilian characteristics of teeth and bony tails; and before they developed sight and hearing far superior to any reptile, a much more efficient brain, feathers, warm blood, the nesting instinct, and air-filled bones. Once all these adaptations were achieved they found themselves in an excellent state to cope comfortably with a wide variety of ecological conditions. At this point a vast diversification set in. Though we do have some valuable fossil guidance for the evolution of the birds up to this point, the picture of their family tree becomes very confused once diversification is under way and we start looking for "missing links."

When the earliest mammals came down from the trees in which they evolved, the evolutionary heyday of the ruling reptiles was already on the wane. As species after species became extinct, the first mammals found the land covered with plants, and buzzing and crawling with insects, worms and spiders; otherwise it was almost empty, with an immense variety of ecological niches waiting to be filled with new species. Once again the earth's prodigiousness and an abated struggle for survival made diversification and an explosive appearance of entirely new forms possible. As soon as these new forms of animal—now mammalian—life became firmly rooted, the number of individuals in each species increased astronomically. Eventually this overcrowding led to a harshening of their ecology, bringing the diversification spree to an end and forcing them into the second, specializing, "horse" type pattern of further evolutionary progress.

While the "struggle for survival" is operative in the "horse" type pattern of evolution, the origin of new genera is almost certainly due to the absence of a severe struggle. On the contrary, it seems that new genera evolve only when ecological pressure is at a minimum. It is food—its lack or abundance—more than anything else which determines the degree of ecological pressure and only to a far lesser extent the exposure to predators.

THE PRIMATES

When a number of still very primitive early mammals descended from the trees to the ground, some forms remained behind and slowly specialized in further development of muscular control and agility, better brains, and more efficient eyes, ears and placentas. These are all evolutionary tendencies which an arboreal habitat fosters much more energetically than life on the ground or in the water.

In the lead in all these developments was a small, mouse-like, insectivorous animal very similar to the surviving East Asiatic tree shrews, whose history can be traced back more than a hundred million years. In fact, their tiny skulls have been found preserved in Mongolian deposits that have been dated as Cretaceous. There is little reason to doubt that about 60 million years ago these tree shrews gave rise to the last explosive diversification among higher mammals: the appearance of the order of Primates. Yet if we accept the view that the primates originated directly from a tree shrew as we know it today, we will land in serious trouble with our interpretation of evolutionary patterns—unless we can find some way of bringing the tree shrew into line.

Our difficulties are twofold. First, the tree shrew has managed to outlive its diversification for tens of millions of years, whereas in all the other cases we have discussed it would seem that the form which burst into diversification became extinct almost immediately. Second, the tree shrew is both arboreal and insectivorous, which means that its ecological margins are very narrow and its struggle for survival extremely harsh.

According to our hypothesis, no animal living such a life can give rise to the luxuriant diversification we find in the order of Primates, which includes such widely different forms as the lemurs, the tarsiers, the primitive New World monkeys, the more advanced Old World monkeys, the great apes, and man, together with countless forms that have suffered extinction and are known to us only from their fossil record. Since it seems utterly impossible that a tree shrew, living a life similar to that of its modern survivors, could have been the starting point from which the primates took their origin; something extraordinary must have happened to the tree shrew of the Eocene before it could embark on such evolutionary exuberance.

At about this time a new type of tree shrew with an entirely different ecology must have arisen, burst into diversification, and suffered early extinction, leaving its own stem-form to continue its existence in the pattern of conservation as we find it today. In the light of our hypothesis, this new and short-lived descendant must have suddenly entered into an ecological Eldorado before it could diversify. There seems to be only one way in which this could have happened—a switch from insectivorous to predominantly herbivorous feeding.

Once this step had been taken, an inexhaustible larder of vast variety was opened to the species. One need but think of the nutritional value of one ripe banana or a sweet mango, which can be eaten in a matter of minutes, compared with the relatively few calories contained in an assortment of flies, beetles, grubs and spiders of the same weight. Moreover, the exertion required to collect such a quantity of insect food is enormous, possibly calling for days of strenuous hunting and searching. It also involves long and risky exposure to predators, of which there were at that time already plenty in the trees such as flesh-eating mammals, snakes, and birds of prey.

The moment fruit, leaves, shoots and bark became staple foods, and insects were only eaten as snacks when our earliest ancestors happened to come upon them or playfully chased them when there was nothing better to do, the grim hunting days were over. Such a small herbivorous animal could easily cover its daily nutritional requirements in a matter of a few minutes without having to stray far from the security of its nest in a hollow tree.

Under such ideal and leisurely ecological conditions there would have been a rapid increase in the number of individuals of the new species and a gradual increase in size, now no longer limited by the exigencies of insectivorous feeding. Among the mutations arising in this population—mutations which would never have had a chance of survival under the stringent conditions of arboreal insectivorous living—some would have proved to be viable under the new wide ecological conditions.

The notion that the primates descended from herbivorous and not insectivorous forefathers is strongly supported by the fact that nearly all primates are predominantly herbivorous. If herbivorous feeding had developed after diversification, we would expect to find some evidence of forms that remained insectivorous until possibly proceeding to become carnivorous. Though man and his immediate ancestors, the tarsiers, and a crab-eating Old World monkey reverted to carnivorous feeding after having been herbivorous for millions of years, there is no evidence that any early primate was predominantly carnivorous. This suggests that the order was herbivorous from the outset.

It is fairly certain that the earliest and most primitive

primates, the lemurs, did not give rise to the tarsiers, the monkeys, the great apes, and man. None of these forms is ancestral to any other, though they probably came from a common stock derived by diversification from a single species. But that species can hardly have been the staid, old, insectivorous tree shrew, although no better fitting ancestor of the primates has as yet been found.

We must remember how very scanty is our fossil record of the primates as compared with that of ground-living animals. Most primates, and certainly all early ones, lived in the trees of tropical forests. Of all media the forest floor is the least favorable for fossilization and only an infinitesimally small part of such regions has been paleontologically explored. Moreover, according to our interpretation of the patterns of evolution the stem-forms that enter into diversification die out rapidly. It would thus be an extraordinarily lucky chance if the fossil remains of such a short-lived "herbivorous tree shrew" had been discovered; and even then there might be little or no evidence to show that it was indeed herbivorous, though it might already have increased in size. But there is as yet no reason to despair.

Other Aspects of Feeding and Evolution

In this chapter we have discussed and speculated on some aspects of the enormous role feeding plays in the process of evolution. It has many other aspects of great importance for the majority of animals, but less for the primates with which alone we shall henceforth be concerned. For instance, the rapid sequence of climatic, botanical and zoological changes that occurred during the Ice

Ages affected the tropical habitat of the primates only in repercussions of greater or lesser rainfall. In most animals, other than primates, the delicate balance between prey and predator, the matter of eating and being eaten, has to some extent influenced the progress of their evolution. But their incredible agility in the trees, superior sight, hearing, and above all the high intelligence of the primates saved them from ever being seriously threatened as a population by the inroads of carnivores; though occasionally they may have become the victims of tree-climbing cats, snakes, and birds of prey.

The following chapters will be devoted to the nutritional habits of the primates from the lemurs to modern man and will try to show how very deep lie the roots of the ways in which we choose our nourishment.

Primate Feeding

IN THIS chapter we will discuss the feeding habits of all the primates excluding man and his immediate ancestors who will be dealt with in the next chapter. We begin with the most primitive primates, the lemurs.

THE LEMURS

Lemurs are relatively small but highly agile, intelligent, tree-living, long-tailed animals. They were once widely spread over all parts of the tropical world in a large variety of species and evidently in considerable numbers. With few exceptions, they are today confined to about 20 species on the island of Madagascar, which became separated from the mainland at a very early date. Thus they were saved from the serious competition of other more highly evolved primates which elsewhere may have brought about their extinction. Outside of Madagascar only the rather more advanced loris of Southern Asia, and the African potto and the bush baby have been able to survive to our day.

For obvious reasons we cannot now know what the earliest and long-extinct lemurs ate, but they were almost certainly predominantly herbivorous. From the habits of surviving forms we may by analogy conclude that like the tree shrews, from which their forefathers descended, they also ate insects. Their dental equipment is suitable for herbivorous as well as carnivorous feeding, and the intestinal equipment of all primates has never gone in for either carnivorous or—more surprisingly—herbivorous specializations. It has always maintained a primitive, halfway or omnivorous structure in spite of millions of years of herbivorous feeding.

In many primates other than man there are vestiges of flesh-eating, and it is possible that in some species this tendency was subsequently further developed, though of this we only have the meager evidence of a few surviving forms. Carnivores have the peculiar habit of suffering extinction much earlier than herbivores; such hypothetical flesh-eating lemurs will therefore have had only a short span of prosperity, and so we may never know.

One of the main difficulties of studying lemurian feeding is that with few exceptions, such as *Propithecus* and *Indris* which are diurnal, lemurs are nocturnal animals living high in the trees of tropical forests. They are thus very hard to watch and a close study of their habits in the wild is extremely arduous. Yet, in 1962, an undaunted French zoologist, J. J. Petter, published a most illuminating study of the lemurs of Madagascar as observed in the

wild, supplemented by valuable observations on the behavior of these animals in captivity. In what follows,
Petter will be our chief authority on the Madagascan
lemurs.

One of the most interesting lemurs is *Daubentonia*,
commonly known as the aye-aye. When an early naturalist's native guide pointed out a member of the species and
whispered "aye aye," meaning "look, look!" the naturalist
thought that this was what the natives called the lemur;
and to this error it owes its common name.

The aye-aye is a small animal about the size of a
domestic cat and has a very bushy tail. Its powerful front
teeth are like those of the rodents, and with them it can
gnaw through hard wood and bark in search of beetle
larvae and even make a hole in a coconut. Another peculi-
arity of the aye-aye is the long and strong middle finger of
its hands which it uses to scoop insects out of their nests, to
empty a bird's egg from its shell, to pick the flesh out of a
coconut, or the brains out of a bird's head. Strangest of all,
the aye-aye uses these fingers, alternating from hand to
hand, to lap up liquids with a rapid succession of flicks
quite similar to the way a cat uses its tongue for the same
purpose.

Though the aye-aye enriches its diet with many and
varied carnivorous snacks, its principal food is vegetarian
and consists of fruit, flowers, and leaves. Madagascan
lemurs on a higher evolutionary scale tend to be more
strictly vegetarian than the primitive species; and as the
aye-aye, judged by its anatomical features, is one of the
most advanced lemurs, its feeding habits are an exception
to this rule.

The two diurnal forms, *Indris* and *Propithecus*, are
strictly vegetarian and have never been seen to eat insects
deliberately, though in captivity they will accept con-
densed milk. *Propithecus* is of special interest because it

can walk on two legs on the ground when it descends from its normal habitat in the trees, showing that a two-legged gait reaches as far back as this still very primitive primate. When walking it balances itself with its arms held high over its head much in the same way that gibbons do.

The less highly evolved nocturnal forms such as *Microcebus, Chierogallus* and *Phaner* have retained mixed feeding. *Microcebus* is astonishingly good at catching flies on the wing with its hands, a skill requiring a sensory and muscular coordination of no mean order. Those species that supplement their diet with moths, crickets, cockroaches and flies eat less bark and leaves than the strictly vegetarian forms. This may be because bark and leaves are richer in insect larvae and eggs than fruit, so that vegetarian lemurs who do not actively catch insects nevertheless get their necessary quota of animal food unwittingly.

Apart from insects, primitive nocturnal lemurs also eat new-born rats and newly hatched birds, which they pick from their nests while foraging at night. They also crush the heads of larger birds and eat their brains, discarding the rest of the carcass. This predeliction for brain is an early forerunner of a common trait among man's immediate ancestors, the australopithecines. It is tempting to believe that this evident need for the constituents of brain tissue arose from the incredible speed with which primate brains evolved.

Advanced nocturnal forms such as *Lepilemur, Avahi* and *Macacus* are finicky, purely vegetarian feeders. They eat tender bark and leaves, flowers and fruit, carefully discarding hard skins and unripe parts. The lemur *Macacus* is particularly fond of cacao beans. It picks them out of the large pods and swallows them whole, apparently for the sake of the mucilaginous substance with which they are covered, as the denuded beans appear intact in the droppings.

Strictly speaking, the lemurs are thus mostly omnivorous, with a strong predominance of vegetable over animal food. This sets them distinctly apart from the entirely insectivorous tree shrews. A strong herbivorous tendency can be followed through all the primates, with possibly the one exception of Tarsius, thus forcefully suggesting that the trait reaches far back into an ancestral form which had acquired this characteristic before it burst into the diversification which led to the new order.

TARSIUS

The tarsiers are much further advanced than the lemurs, particularly as regards the development of the brain. They were once spread far and wide in many species, but are today reduced to a single species, a rare rat-like animal, *Tarsius spectrum,* that lives only in Malay and Indo-China. It is a highly specialized primate, having developed long hind legs for a jumping gait, suckers on its toes and huge forward-looking, nocturnal eyes. It is known to eat insects and small lizards. It is not certain that it lives on such food exclusively, though its small size makes this possible. More observations of its life in the wild are needed to settle this question—observations that are handicapped by its rarity, its nocturnal habits and the fact that it lives high up in the trees of dense tropical forests.

THE NEW WORLD MONKEYS

The New World monkeys differ in many respects from the more advanced Old World monkeys. They have widely separated nostrils which face laterally, relatively small jaws, and their ears lack the pointed tip found in the Old World monkeys. Most of them have what amounts to a fifth limb in their prehensile tail by which they can swing on a branch and with which they are able to grasp food. Their buttocks do not have the callosities seen in the Old World monkeys; their thumbs cannot be fully opposed to the other fingers of their hands, while their big toes are mobile and can be opposed to the other toes. Their nails are narrow and in the marmosets have become claws. There are many other anatomical differences, suggesting that the New World monkeys came from an ancestral stock of their own formed at the time of primate diversification. Moreover, they are all strictly tree-living and inhabit the forests of South America.

Among the New World monkeys only one species, Aotus or *Nictipithecus,* is nocturnal; in fact, it is the only existing nocturnal monkey. Aotus has large, forward-looking eyes, which have squeezed the nasal area and pushed it forward so that the nose somewhat resembles that of an Old World monkey. Its sense of smell is far better developed than that of other monkeys which is undoubtedly important for nocturnal feeding, though judged by the general trends in primate evolution this must be considered a primitive feature. Like less advanced nocturnal lemurs, Aotus feeds on fruit, young birds, and insects which it chases during most of the night.

Even more avidly insectivorous are the tiny squirrel

monkeys, but for them too the vegetable kingdom supplies most of their caloric requirements. The long-limbed spider monkeys, on the other hand, are almost exclusively fruit-eating, as is also the howler monkey, the largest of all American monkeys. Compared with Afro-Asian monkeys, the New World monkeys are a noisy lot; and the howler monkeys are by far the noisiest of all primates, even surpassing man. They owe this vociferous propensity to the peculiar structure of their larynx, and the din they create at dawn can be heard for miles. Their howling is a manifestation of the territorial instinct by which they regulate the size of the population strictly in accordance with the availability of food.

Except for the howler monkeys whose behavior in the wild has been very carefully studied by Carpenter, competent observations on other New World monkeys in the wild state are still sketchy, and it is probable that many interesting facets remain to be discovered. It does, however, seem unlikely that anything of basic importance for our particular inquiry will emerge from such studies. Again we see a large assortment of primates which are all, at least potentially, omnivorous, with a heavy predominance of vegetarian feeding and a varying degree of insectivorous and even carnivorous supplementary alimentation.

THE OLD WORLD MONKEYS

In most respects the Old World monkeys are more advanced than those living on the American continent. They do not have prehensile tails, but their brains are better. They have a strong trend towards the sitting posture and have developed callosities on their buttocks, though it is by no means certain—and perhaps not even probable—that this is an adaptation to the use of the buttocks as a seat. However that may be, the sitting posture freed the forelimbs for play, feeding, and searching each other for fleas and the salt crystals that remain from evaporated sweat—activities which greatly fostered the evolution of their brains.

They also produced the first truly ground-living primates—the gregarious baboons. Though baboons are predominantly herbivorous, they are not averse to carnivorous feeding on insects, birds, amphibia and small reptiles; they will even occasionally kill and devour domestic sheep. Baboons live in a strictly hierarchical social organization. Individuals readily sacrifice themselves for the welfare of the troop and generously help any member who finds himself in trouble. Compared with other Old World monkeys, the baboon's brain is not outstandingly developed, but it strikes us as being extremely intelligent, probably because the behavioral consequences of living on the ground and its social organization are quite similar to those of primitive man.

As a general rule Old World monkeys are frugivorous and have large cheek pouches in which they can store a considerable amount of food. An exception to this rule are the langurs, to which group the famous Hanuman monkeys of India belong, in whose likeness the deity Hanuman—the monkey god of the Hindu pantheon—is represented. The langurs' life is arboreal and they live mostly on leaves. They are among the very few primates which show some beginnings of intestinal adaptation to herbivorous feeding, having particularly large and sacculated stomachs which compensate them for the lack of cheek pouches. Two other species, closely related to the langurs, show the same feature. One is the large *Rhinopithecus* known as the snub-nosed monkey of Northwestern China and Tibet, which has a concave nose with an upturned point. Strangely enough, the other form also has a very peculiar nose unique among monkeys. Its scientific name is *Nasalis larvatus* (hidden nose) which too is odd, as nothing is more prominent than its nose; in fact, it is elongated into a sort of trunk, which in old males hangs down over the mouth. Another species, interesting from a nutritional point of view, is *Macacus cynomologus*, the crab-eating monkey of India which lives, if not exclusively, certainly to a large extent, on land crabs and such crustaceans as it can collect from the water's edge.

Since fruit and nuts are highly nutritious and always available in their habitat, monkeys have plenty of leisure and are wasteful feeders. If something attracts their ever alert attention or they stop to follow a whim of the moment they will either drop whatever they are eating or tuck what they can into their cheek pouches for later reconsideration. Contrary to that of most animals, their feeding seems casual. It is not performed in deadly earnest nor with complete concentration. When a monkey eats, its eyes are looking round with lively interest in its surroundings. While all lemurs, tarsiers, and the New World monkeys commonly eat without using their hands, this is quite exceptional in the Old World monkeys who normally feed from hand to mouth in a sitting posture.

THE APES

The four surviving apes, the acrobatic, slender gibbon, the red-haired, ponderous orangutan, the quick-witted, lively chimpanzee, and the mighty, awe-inspiring gorilla are all essentially vegetarians, though, as with other primates, an occasional insect or a small fleshy snack are not unwelcome. They are all tailless; and though the gibbon can walk upright on the ground with its long brachiating arms flailing above its head and the orang ambles along supported by the knuckles of its hands, both are quite predominantly arboreal and little interested in what food the ground has to offer.

The chimpanzee and the gorilla, who are both fairly comfortable on two legs, are largely ground-living. The feeding of the apes is even more casual than that of the monkeys, and it is easy to follow the path taken by a gorilla family by noting the half-eaten fruit they discard on their way through the jungle. They will grab a fruit, take a bite or two, then lose interest and throw the perfectly edible remainder away. They never make a meal of available food, but prefer to take a snack or a nibble here and there as they move along.

With the possible exception of the gibbon, apes in captivity share with many monkeys and to some extent with human infants a remarkable interest in their own excreta. They lap up their urine and frequently eat their own feces, with which they also play and besmear themselves. So common is this behavior that it is hard to believe that it has anything to do with the boredom of captivity, yet I have not read about observations of this kind in the wild. It would be interesting, particularly with regard to human infants and small children, to know how and why such behavior originated. Possibly the urine is drunk for its high salt content. Like human beings, apes also eat their nasal pickings.

Captive chimpanzees will use a stick to get at a banana and learn to pile up boxes to reach a tempting reward. Under experimental conditions at the sight of a chained leopard, their traditionally most dangerous enemy, they will pick up a stick provided for them with every sign of rage; but perhaps their most natural use of a tool is to catch ants. They take a small stick, wet it with saliva by drawing it through their mouth, and then hold it in the path of the ants. As these swarm over it, the chimp strips them off with his lips and replaces the stick for more. He may continue this ant-catching for hours, deeply absorbed and not at all casual as he is when eating fruit. The shades of the old tree shrew are still with him.

Yet if a chimp is offered a piece of raw meat, he will show no nutritional interest, even if he is hungry. Why? His teeth are perfectly adequate to deal with flesh and his intestinal tract should have no difficulty digesting it. I do not know whether the experiment has ever been tried, but it would seem that if at weaning a baby chimp is removed from the tutelage of its mother, it could be healthily reared on a carefully prepared and supplemented, predominantly carnivorous diet.

This brings us to the knotty problem of how an ape's feeding habits originate—how much is inherited, i.e., determined by genes, and how much is learned. The question is difficult to answer because genetic factors are also involved in learning and obviously determine the degree of learning ability, but to what extent the subject matter of learning is genetic is hard to say. Even the greatest learner, the human child, produces quite different results, in spite of uniform tuition for languages or mathematics.

Genetic factors are certainly at play in these differences of ability in certain fields of learning.

Without any tuition, bees build hives, and birds build nests characteristic of their species. A horse will take to grass and a lion to flesh. Such behavior is not learned, though the females of carnivora do teach their cubs the technique of the chase. But when we come to potential omnivora such as the primates, who need prolonged maternal care, we cannot be so sure. Here it is conceivable that training and the early establishment of conditioned reflexes enter strongly into the formation of the final feeding pattern. Once established, this will remain immutable and be passed on in infancy to the next generation.

Only in the very long run does the availability of one or another type of food lead to a selective preference. Very gradually there is a favoring of certain, at first rudimentary, trends towards a better adjustment to changing ecological conditions. But in the animal world an individual will never decide to make such an adjustment in matters of feeding. It will always starve to death in the midst of plentiful potential food if this food is not included in its instinctive or conditioned menu. It requires a much higher degree of abstract reasoning power than even an ape possesses to step out of an ingrained behavior pattern by an act of will. Man alone with his infinitely superior brain has this ability and even in man it requires an outstanding intelligence to accomplish such a feat.

In the next chapter we shall discuss how very important this ability may have been in the evolution of *Homo sapiens*.

Earliest Human Feeding

THE EVOLUTIONARY point at which a so-called "ape-man" ceases by definition to be an ape and becomes a man is still being discussed with asperity. Some years ago Dr. Kenneth Oakley, head of the Paleoanthropological Department of the British Museum, made a very sensible suggestion. He proposed that we should arbitrarily decide to call any creature that purposefully manufactured tools human, and any creature that did not indulge in this activity an ape. The term tools was taken to mean stone tools, pebble tools, hand axes, scrapers, etc.; until quite recently this suggestion was generally accepted. The fact that wooden tools such as spears, clubs and bamboo knives, were fashioned ages before flints were chipped was deliberately ignored, because of them no traces remained.

For some time there could be no objection to such an anthropological convention. But then Prof. Raymond Dart of the Witwatersrand University of Johannesburg pro-

duced convincing evidence that the South African australopithecines deliberately collected and fashioned certain
bones of certain animals for use as tools. Hitherto the
australopithecines had been classified as apes; but if
Oakley's criterion of manhood—namely the purposeful
making of tools—was to be adhered to, they certainly
qualified for this distinction.

Those australopithecines whose remains have been
found in many parts of Central and South Africa were
extraordinarily man-like. They ran and walked on two legs
and as hunters they were quite predominantly carnivorous. They stood about four feet high, had a much larger
brain than an ape of comparable size and were slender and
agile. Though this cannot be proved, we may safely assume
that they made use of wooden tools such as sharp and easily
made bamboo knives.

The australopithecines flourished over a million years
ago, and they had a contemporary known as *Paranthropus*.
Both *Paranthropus* and the pithecines seem to have descended from a Miocene ape, known as Proconsul, already
more man-like than any surviving ape. Quite unlike the
nimble pithecines, *Paranthropus* was a heavy, clumsy vegetarian with huge teeth and in all these respects more
closely resembled the common ancestor Proconsul. As a
vegetarian, *Paranthropus* had little or no use for tools
which are the prerequisite of hunting flesh eaters and this
leads to an interesting speculation.

In the Olduvai Gorge, Louis S. B. Leakey found a frag-
mented skull of *Paranthropus* (which he calls *Sinjan-
thropus*), together with primitive pebble tools. It was
therefore assumed that this *Paranthropus* was the maker of
these tools which, according to the foregoing observations
seems most unlikely. It might therefore be argued that
these tools were made by pithecines which had a long history of hunting and that this *Paranthropus,* found among

the remains of many other animals, was one of their victims. We know that the pithecines liked to eat the brains of baboons so that the much larger brain of *Paranthropus* might well have tempted them. Moreover, a troop of these highly agile hunters should have had little difficulty in stoning the more ponderous *Paranthropus* to death.

The fact that no pithecine bones have been found in this Olduvai deposit does not necessarily mean that pithecines were not there. This particular area was at that time exceedingly rich in game so that there may have been less need for cannibalism than at other sites where it was very prevalent. It is also conceivable that the pithecines did not live and die at their slaughtering sites—a possibility which might explain why so many coprolites of hyenas are found among the remains of their feasts. These coprolites became quite famous in paleoanthropological circles, because Prof. Dart's critics hotly contended that the peculiar fragmentation of the bones he had found had been produced not by pithecines but by hyenas; a view which has now been definitely ruled out. It seems much more likely that the hyenas sneaked into these places at night when they were deserted to feed on the rapidly rotting leftovers as is their habit. It even seems possible that all the pithecine bones found on the sites where they slaughtered belong to victims of cannibalism and that the pithecines disposed of such of their own dead as they did not eat in some other way that left no trace. Judging by the amount of animal bones found on these sites, they must have been occupied for very long periods of time, and if it had been a pithecine habit to leave their dead in such unsavory surroundings, one would expect to find far more pithecine bones than one actually does.

BRAIN SIZE AND INTELLIGENCE

One of the chief arguments against giving the pithe-cines human status was that their brains were considered too small. It was held that a creature having a brain volume of 850–950 cc, as against modern man's 1500 cc and a gorilla's maximum of 850 cc, could not possibly be classified as human.

Actually the size of a brain has nothing to do with its intellectual efficiency. Thus an elephant with a ten-pound brain or a whale with a twenty-pound one is not nearly as intelligent as a marmoset with a brain weighing only a few grams. Similarly the first electronic computers were huge unwieldy contraptions, involving a fantastic waste of space and energy and yet they were far less efficient than modern circuits that can be crammed together to occupy the space of a brick. It is true that a marmoset is a tiny animal compared with an elephant or a whale, but it is also true that no fixed ratio between body size and brain size can be established. For instance the whale has 1 gm. of brain for every kilogram of body weight. Modern man has 1 gm. of brain for every 44 gm. of body weight and thus con-siderably outdoes the whale. But some New World mon-keys, the capuchins for instance, have a ratio of 1 gm. of brain for every 17.5 gm. of body weight and should there-fore, by this reckoning, be about three times as intelligent as *Homo sapiens,* which is obviously nonsense.

Already, in 1956, Prof. Dart administered what ought to have been the *coup-de-grâce* to all this wrangling about brain size versus intelligence in a delightfully erudite paper, but apparently the question's ghost still haunts some scientific cloisters.

Intelligence depends entirely on the number of neurons contained in a brain. Neurons are microscopic nerve centers which have been compared to the transistors in an electronic computer. They are localized chiefly in the covering of the brain, the gray matter or cortex. The number of neurons which can be accommodated in a brain of a given size depends on their density, the thickness of the cortex, and the extent of its surface, which in turn depends much more on the number and depth of the folds or convolutions than on the overall volume of the brain. The modern human brain has been calculated to contain some 7–8,000 million neurons. Under the microscope the very thick human cortex appears packed with them, while the cortex of a gorilla is much thinner and has only a small fraction of this number.

No one has ever seen the brain of an australopithecine; and though it has been claimed that some conclusions on the convolutions can be drawn from the conformation of the inside of the cranium, no conclusions about their depth or the thickness of the cortex—much less its neuron content—can be reached by the examination of the fossilized cranium of an extinct species. We know that carnivorous feeding which involves hunting, and in the case of the pithecines, the making of tools and weapons, operates strongly as a selective factor favoring better brains, an advantage of which the more brutish vegetarian *Paranthropus* could not avail himself. It is, therefore, perfectly legitimate to suggest that the pithecines had a much more deeply convoluted brain with a thicker cortex containing far more neurons than a gorilla with a brain of the same size. This would mean that the pithecines would then have had an intelligence far superior to any estimate based on the comparative size of their brain.

THE CARNIVOROUS SWITCH

It is certain that modern man with all his intellectual attributes and his astonishing manual dexterity could never have evolved directly out of herbivorous ancestors. Only after they had accomplished the transition from herbivorous to carnivorous feeding did our ancestors become toolmakers. It would therefore seem most logical to postdate the beginnings of manhood to this carnivorous switch, a feat which no other primate seems to have been able to perform. This event, laden with unforeseeable consequences, probably took place in the latter part of the Pliocene epoch in Central Africa.

During the preceding Miocene—that is, 10–20 million years ago—this part of the globe was covered with dense tropical rain forests, and it was there that Proconsul lived. But towards the close of the Miocene and throughout the whole Pliocene, which lasted until about one million years ago, the rainfall became less and less. The forest slowly changed to a savannah landscape, then became riverine where trees could only survive along the banks of dwindling lakes and rivers, until towards the end of the Pliocene the whole landscape became so arid that few plants other than cacti could exist. These slow but nonetheless dramatic events, together with many other points that we shall touch upon in this chapter, have been vividly described by Robert Ardrey in his fascinating book *African Genesis.*

The changes in climate and vegetation spelled Proconsul's doom. Well adapted to forest life, he was unable to survive in sparsely wooded surroundings. But before he departed forever from the scene he—or perhaps his ancestors—had evolved new forms such as the dryopithecines, *Paranthropus* and the forerunners of the australopithecines, all of which were presumably, like Proconsul, herbivorous. The decline in edible vegetation appears to have driven the dryopithecines away from Central Africa into a wide dispersal all over the Eurasian continent, where climate and flora were more congenial. In some of these places, such as the foothills of the Himalayas, dryopithecines were able to survive for a long time. *Paranthropus* seems to have had less wanderlust and may have suffered his decline and fall in Africa, though, as we shall presently see, it is just possible that he too found a niche as yet undiscovered, and that he may have been concerned with the origin of *Homo neanderthalensis.*

That the pithecines alone were able to thrive in the inhospitable Pliocene Africa is almost certainly due to the fact that they became carnivorous at an early date. This is such a momentous step in primate evolution that the temptation to speculate on how it came about is irresistible. Throughout the whole wide range of primates from lemurs to apes rudiments of insectivorous and occasionally carnivorous feeding were never quite lost and their dental and digestive equipment remained potentially omnivorous. Therefore one might think that in a situation of ecological duress these carnivorous rudiments could have been developed in a slow and painful process for which a few million years were available. In the evolutionary scale, however, a few million years seem hardly enough to bring about such a deeply incisive change in a species that multiplied at a very slow rate. Even the comparatively minor switch from browsing to grazing which the horses achieved during the Miocene took many millions of years to complete. Nor can we resort to a mutational hypothesis. We cannot assume that a carnivorous mutation suddenly appeared and thrived while the non-mutated vegetarian forms died out. It is inconceivable that a gene mutation could bring about such a complete reversal of a whole, complex, instinct pattern, canceling all the postnatal influences of training and conditioning of the young by their parents or the troop. Perhaps something like this could happen in very much lower animals, but it is unthinkable in a mammal, particularly an ape.

We may ask why no other ape or monkey that shared the pithecines' drought-ridden habitat was able to accomplish a similar feat before being forced into extinction or dispersal into more hospitable climes. As we may never know exactly when, how, and what happened; and as it is our conceited nature to feel more comfortable within the framework of even the flimsiest hypothesis, provided it does not all too seriously impinge upon scientific probability; we are free to reconstruct the following exciting story.

We can imagine a clan of early, still vegetarian pithecines hungrily wandering over the dry earth in search of edible vegetation. They have finished what the edge of their last waterhole had to offer. Dimly their leader remembers another waterhole where food was once plentiful and he leads his troop there. At last they arrive starving, parched, and weak and stagger to the water's edge to quench their thirst. They drop back on their haunches and look hungrily around. All they see is thorny bushes, some grass, spreading weeds, and cactus.

As they gaze hopelessly over the water, they watch the frogs, the fish; the turtles. They see some animals come to drink, an otter shoots through the water with a big fish in its mouth, storks and herons alight, and as they wade they deftly pick frogs and fish which they swallow with relish. Remembering how often a single human genius has changed our destiny, let us suppose that the leader of the clan is a pithecine genius and let us endow him with some dim powers of reasoning. He watches the feeding of these many animals and sees that they are strong and healthy. He is probably used to eating fat grubs, the egg-laden abdomens of locusts, a handful of ants, and perhaps eggs. Like all the higher primates, he is also inquisitive and imitative. Suddenly he is struck by the idea of copying the otter. He steps into the water and has soon caught a fish. With his teeth he tears out a piece of flesh. It is good to have something solid to chew and swallow, and he eats more. He catches a second and a third fish, and suddenly the gnawing hunger is gone.

Two young males now imitate their leader, invite their females to join them, and soon they are stuffing chewed raw fish into the mouths of their starving offspring. The clan now no longer suffers either thirst or hunger. They rapidly fill out and live for a long time near this new inexhaustible source of food. They no longer need to limit their numbers the way all animals do when threatened with food shortage. They can now breed freely and the clan grows rapidly. Soon it splits up into new nuclei of now fully carnivorous troops, which in turn thrive. By a single act of what we can but call genius they have changed a hopeless ecological situation into sudden abundance.

In a further sequence of brilliant ideas they discover the use of tools and thereby rapidly enrich their menu with larger and faster game. They become fiercer and stronger; their wits, their eyes, ears, and muscular co-ordination are sharpened to their physiological limits by daily training in the chase. The degree of hunting ability will for the first time have become a powerfully operative factor in sexual selection, leading to ever greater manual and intellectual skill. Gradually their vegetarian brethren who lacked a genius in their midst will have died out, leaving the field entirely to the new carnivorous species; these indeed may have soon learned to prey on them, initiating the trend to cannibalism, which has always been a prominent feature of the feeding of man and his ancestors.

This story may be a myth, but something very similar often occurs in our own day. Let us take the case of a scion of an old and strictly orthodox Hindu Brahmin family. For possibly 2500 years—about a hundred generations—none of his ancestors will ever have eaten even a morsel of flesh, fish, fowl, egg, or insect. Their only source of animal food will have been milk. The idea of eating even a scrap of meat or food that has been contaminated is so utterly revolting to the young Hindu that the mere thought may make him vomit. With him it is not only a matter of religious prohibition; it is a strong repugnance which he feels to be entirely physical. I know from personal experience that it is not uncommon for an orthodox Hindu to prefer dying of pernicious anemia to taking liver extract.

Our youngster happens to be particularly bright, and so his family is at long last and very reluctantly persuaded to send him to England for further studies. There he soon finds that his dietary habits complicate his life, restrict him in all social activities connected with food and drink and set him aside from his English companions so that he is forced to keep to the company of his own kind. But he is steeped in western civilization and impatient of the age-old patterns of life as it is led in his Indian home. Yet he cannot at first bring himself to abandon his strictly vegetarian habits.

But one day he does decide to take the dietary plunge that will integrate him into the life led by those around him. With a supreme effort of will, he suppresses his repugnance and bolts a few bits of rare steak. That night he feels a little odd, a little apprehensive, a little guilty, a little rash; but nothing alarming happens. So he tries again, with the same courage that we would need to eat stewed rats or roast poodle. Then he has eggs and bacon for breakfast, and learns to dissect a fried sole and to pick the flesh off chicken bones. In a surprisingly short time his feeding habits have undergone a most dramatic change. He feels none the worse for it and now finds himself able to enjoy all the advantages that conformity brings with it.

Similarly, an Eskimo, conditioned for tens of thousands of years to live on fish, seal and blubber, would be none the worse if he were suddenly switched to the Brahmin's diet. He would surely balk psychologically, but he would be able to overcome his primary reluctance by an effort of will if circumstances warranted his doing so. No ape would be capable of such an intellectual feat.

Somewhere along the line of pithecine or pre-pithecine evolution the carnivorous switch must have taken place and it presupposes a higher intellectual capacity than we have hitherto been willing to grant these creatures. It was also the evolutionary step that more than any other led to the use and manufacture of tools on an ever widening scale. It is the use of tools that made pithecine survival and the further evolution to *Homo sapiens* possible. So to repeat, it seems reasonable to postdate the origin of man to the carnivorous switch and not to consider the first evidence of manufactured stone implements as a starting point.

CANNIBALISM

Once it was discovered that the flesh of animals is an excellent food, the step to cannibalism was a short one. Cannibalism was certainly practiced by the australopithecines and has since been a universal trait of the human race.

I knew an old gentleman who liked to tell the story of his visit to New Guinea as a young man to establish a trading station among the Papuans. He found that he was always able to pick the cannibals in a group of villagers by their ferocious look. In every case, so he proudly recounts, the "monsters" admitted that he was right. But it never occurred to him to ask the fairest maidens. Had he done so, he would have discovered much to his surprise that they too were "monsters."

In a careful study of cannibalism by Garry Hogg published in 1958, the pious notion that eating human flesh was always a sort of ceremony or ritualistic performance was definitely proved to be wrong. Cannibalism was almost everywhere considered a gastronomic feast and the participants claimed that human flesh tasted better than any other meat. In most cases ritual embellishments were secondary; the idea that the stout heart of a warrior passed on to him that ate it was a principle quite generally applied also to the organs of animals, and of this superstition vestiges still exist in modern man.

Children of captive women were bred for the pot, and when the slain and the murdered were in abundance their flesh was bartered to other tribes. Where there was a shortage of flesh from larger animals, neighboring clans staged fights, often urged on by their womenfolk, for the express purpose of eating the clansmen that fell in battle. It was common practice to break the arms and legs of prospective victims to prevent their escape, to dismember them, and to roast and eat their limbs while they were still alive and to joke and laugh about the victims' suffering. From the many authentic reports that we have from persons who have witnessed such scenes in many parts of the world, the extraordinary indifference with which the victims seem to face their fate is repeatedly stressed. It seems to be an almost universal trait of man that, where his food is concerned, he is the most cruel, callous, and vicious creature imaginable. In what we define as uncivilized society, little or no difference is made or felt between animal and man, once they are destined to be eaten.

Only the Buddhists and, following their example, the Brahmins, Jains, and a few modern individuals, who are generally regarded as faddists, uphold the tenet that it is wrong to take any kind of life or that man is vegetarian by his nature. In the case of the Eastern vegetarians there is, apart from the general ethical principle, another strong motive for not killing animals. They believe in the transmigration of the soul and that it may be reincarnated in the body of an animal. Thus they might unwittingly kill and eat a reincarnated ancestor or a beloved member of their family who has recently passed away.

From Pithecanthropus to Homo Sapiens

The next known step in human evolution was achieved in *Pithecanthropus,* of whom remains have been found over most of the Old World from Eastern China to Java, from Central Africa to the Mediterranean, and in Heidelberg in Germany. In *Pithecanthropus* the jaws have receded further into the face and the volume of the brain has increased. It seems much more likely that these forms descended from the pithecines than from the *Paranthropus* branch. They have gone far beyond the early pebble tool stage and have already begun fashioning stone implements of relatively high artisanship. But perhaps their most important cultural contribution is the domestication of fire.

We can only speculate how this was achieved: from volcanoes which seems the most probable; or from forest fires caused by lightning, autocombustion, dry branches rubbing together in the wind, or very occasionally meteorites. At first fire was collected, transported and kept going. Only very much later did man, by a stroke of genius, learn how to kindle it. Until quite recently there were still tribes in the Andamans and among the Papuans who had not yet learned this art and who depended for their fire entirely on other tribes that lived on volcanic slopes.

Apart from the protection against cold and wild beasts which fire afforded, its domestication had a profound effect on human feeding. Most early cooking was done by roasting on a spit, by burying meat between hot stones or similarly baking it in a covering of clay. Boiling food cannot have played a great role, as pottery was still tens of thousands of years away, though it is conceivable that the shells of giant ostrich eggs or the human cranium placed on hot stones found early use. It was also discovered that water can be heated in a hole lined with clay by throwing hot stones into it.

From *Pithecanthropus* on, the threads of human evolution again become thin, tangled, and as yet unraveled. We know much more about the stone implements made during this period than the anatomical characteristics of their makers. This anthropological twilight continues until the

Neanderthalers begin their wide diffusion in Europe, North Africa, and the Near East. With the Neanderthalers we are today on rather firm ground, owing to the large number of their remains discovered. They were carnivorous and fairly good hunters. They made stone implements of many kinds, used fire, and are the first in the human line of descent that were able to live near the fringe of the ice that covered northern Europe at that time. They were cave dwellers and inveterate cannibals. Their brain was considerably larger than that of *Pithecanthropus,* though still far short of modern man; and it is understandable that when Neanderthal remains were first unearthed it was believed that they were the direct ancestors of *Homo sapiens.*

While it is arguable that the Neanderthalers evolved out of descendants of *Paranthropus* who were somewhere, somehow able to survive and belatedly turned carnivorous, the Neanderthalers can, by reason of their anatomy, certainly not have been ancestral to Cro-Magnon man who succeeded them and is the direct ancestor of modern man. If we leave out the Neanderthalers, there seems to be a more direct line from *Australopithecus* to *Pithecanthropus* to Cro-Magnon-like forms that are known to have existed contemporarily with the Neanderthalers and the Cro-Magnons themselves. Here again though it is just possible that at the fringe of the rapid Cro-Magnon expansion from somewhere in Asia, there was some interbreeding with the Neanderthalers and that this led to such races as the Australian bushmen, the Ceylonese Veddahs, and perhaps others.

The Cro-Magnons appeared in Europe about 40,000 years ago. They were immensely superior to the Neanderthalers, both as artisans and as hunters, suggesting that they came from very early carnivorous stock such as the pithecines. Their brains were about as big as those of modern man; it is assumed that they already had the rudiments of true speech; and among them there were remarkable artists and their style and skill seems to have been long preserved among the African bushmen who had a skin of an almost golden color. The Cro-Magnons were much taller than the Neanderthalers. They had high-domed foreheads, and for the first time, a projecting chin. To the Neanderthalers they must have appeared to be strange and terrifying supermen against whom resistance was hopeless.

It would take us too far afield to discuss the still very unclear origin of human races. They all belong to the same species which we call *Homo sapiens*. They were all at one time killers and cannibals whose intake of vegetable food was very limited, and it was not until the Neolithic revolution some 10,000 years ago that all this changed for those who were able to shake off their paleolithic shackles.

The Neolithic Revolution

THE TERM *Neolithic* (late Stone Age) does not do justice to the vast cultural strides made in the few thousand years between the *Mesolithic* (middle Stone Age) and the Age of Metals. During the Neolithic age the ancient stone tool industry became highly perfected: fine polishing of stone surfaces was obtained; wooden handles were fitted to elegantly shaped stone axes; and wooden shafts to stone spearheads and arrowheads. The Neolithic patterns for these tools were faithfully copied in copper, bronze and iron when metal began to replace stone.

Yet the changes brought about by improved techniques of working with stone were not nearly as important as the Neolithic inventions of agriculture, the domestication of animals, and pottery. These are inventions quite comparable in their cultural significance to engines and motors, electricity, flight, rocket propulsion, and nuclear fission in our own age, and can only have been conceived and executed by an imposing array of geniuses.

For some not yet fully understood reason this new creativeness seems to have started almost simultaneously in South America, in the Indus Valley of India and, best known to us, in the area between Palestine and the western border of Iran, which includes Mesopotamia. Perhaps the receding ice of the last glaciation had something to do with it. As the fringe of the ice retreated towards the north, these areas received more rainfall. Fauna and flora became so abundant that the sparse human populations found hunting and food-gathering easier than before. They therefore had much more leisure to observe, play, and experiment in their environment with quite spectacular results.

AGRICULTURE

In the Near East wheat and barley grew wild, and even as far back as Mesolithic times they were collected, mashed with water to a paste and baked on hot stones. Some grains were scattered round the camp sites and in the next season they germinated and grew. This had probably happened untold times without being noticed, because at that time the natural function of a seed was completely unknown.

Only a quite outstanding intellect can have brought the accidentally scattered seed into causal relationship with the plants that grew on the camp site and drawn the brilliant conclusion that the scattering could be done deliberately to his profit. One can well imagine how fiercely the duller clansmen and the women who had laboriously gathered the wild grain must have opposed such an experiment. To them it must have seemed sheer lunacy to waste valuable food in such a way. Yet some men or women did have the courage to persevere, in spite of ridicule, and it is thanks to them that agriculture was born. When the experiment proved to be highly successful, the onerous and time-consuming drudgery of gathering wild grains changed from a chore into festive harvesting. The news of this stupendous discovery evidently spread like wildfire to other clans.

The cultivation of rice in the Indus Valley—and somewhat later the growing of maize in Central America—probably started in a similar way, quite independently of what was going on in Mesopotamia. Once the basic idea had been conceived and proven, a vast array of other food plants were rapidly taken into cultivation. When the harvest was in, the camp moved to a new site, until it was discovered that by turning over the earth the same plot could be used year after year. This discovery made fixed settlements possible, and it is the starting point of Neolithic urbanization. In Asia, fruit, millet, lentils, beans, and soya beans were early agricultural products; while in Central America, potatoes, sunflowers, tomatoes, stringbeans, groundnuts, avocado, papaya, pineapple, and above all maize were cultivated. Fruit-growers learned the art of grafting, and by a long process of careful selection new and better varieties of plants were raised. These were then crossed for hardiness and better yields. The value of artificial fertilization was discovered after some brilliant thinker noticed that fields on which sheep or cattle had been kept were more fertile than others. In Central America, it was discovered that burying fish under the roots of a plant improved its yield.

ALCOHOL

When grains are mashed, mixed with water, and left standing—particularly in a warm climate—they rapidly ferment and produce alcohol. The consumption of alcohol is at least as old as agriculture and probably much older, as diluted honey and tapped palm sap ferment readily producing a highly intoxicating beverage. Similarly fruit, tubers and the fleshy flowers of the Mohar tree, the Indian "flame of the forest," can be used for fermentation. In these pre-pottery days hides supported on sticks or clay-lined holes in the ground may have served as recipients. The art of distillation, which was the first deliberate chemical operation performed by man, came much later.

The drinking of fermented liquors has a very important nutritional aspect quite apart from caloric value and the intoxicating property of alcohol. This is the high nutritional value of the yeast which causes the fermentation. What happened on the small South Pacific island of Nauru is a case in point. The island had belonged to Germany and then became an Australian protectorate after World War I. All remained peaceful until someone discovered rich deposits of phosphates that could be mined and sold as chemical fertilizers. Since time immemorial the inhabitants of Nauru had been drinking the fermented sap of their coconut palms, and they often got drunk. The mining company depended on native labor and deplored this state of affairs, both from an economic and a humanitarian point of view. Prohibition was therefore introduced in the whole island, and the collecting of sap from the crowns of the palms was stopped. The population became gratifyingly sober, but the mining company's troubles were by no means over.

Not long after prohibition was strictly enforced, there appeared an alarming rise in infant mortality. The company therefore called upon an eminent nutritionist to come to Nauru and investigate. He quickly diagnosed the cause of death among the children as infantile beri-beri, a disease due to a deficiency of vitamin B in their mother's milk. A careful study of native feeding habits then showed that their diet was highly deficient in vitamin B, and that by far the most important source of this essential vitamin was their forbidden palm sap toddy. Prohibition was therefore immediately repealed, and within a year the infant mortality was back to its former level. Again there were some cases of drunkenness, but children no longer died of what had seemed a mysterious disease. Today Nauru is a thriving island clamoring for independence and a seat of its own in the United Nations.

When the Indian government introduced prohibition at the instigation of Gandhi, whose son was an alcoholic, it meant a tremendous sacrifice in badly needed revenue. Prohibition might have been justified on ethical grounds had it been confined to distilled liquors, bottled beer and wine, but unfortunately it was also extended to fermented palm sap toddy. This deprived many of the coastal inhabitants of a very important source of the vitamin B complex, and the professional toddy-tappers of their livelihood.

Particularly for the latter reason, endless experiments were conducted to market fresh unfermented palm sap, a delicious, sour-sweet, non-alcoholic drink. This involved the daily sterilization and chemical treatment of the toddy pots that are hung in the crowns of the palms, and refrigeration of the sap as soon as it was tapped to keep it from fermenting, an entirely impracticable procedure in rural India. Gandhi himself drank this so-called *nira* early in the morning, but as it had received no special treatment, fermentation was by then well under way and so—unknown to him—his breakfast drink already contained about 4 per cent alcohol. Instead of the old toddy shops, *nira* shops were opened under government control. The sugary sap, when free of alcohol, made a magnificent nutrient medium for all kinds of bacteria, and when outbreaks of typhoid and cholera were traced to the *nira* shops, they were hurriedly shut down. At the time, a Bombay cartoonist drew a picture of a corpse being carried away from a *nira* shop with the legend: *nira* (pronounced neera) my God to Thee.

The Domestication of Animals

The first animals to be domesticated were the dogs that scavenged around Mesolithic camps. In Central America, dogs were bred for food and in China, chow puppies are still considered a delicacy; but elsewhere the dog's nutritional importance lies in its ability to help the hunter and the herdsman. The use of dogs for drawing sleds dates very far back. It is possible that the ancient Egyptian dogs were bred from jackals, but the wolf seems to be the ancestor of all European dogs.

Sheep and goats were the next animals to be tamed at the beginning of the Neolithic age or about 6000 B.C. Both sheep and goats lived wild in the Near East and some domestication may have occurred there; but far more successful were the Asiatic species, such as the moufflon, which were domesticated in the east and then spread rapidly westwards. Pigs were domesticated from two wild species, *Sus scrofa vittatus* and *Sus scrofa scrofa*. Vittatus is indigenous to Southeastern Asia and is the only important animal to have been domesticated by the Chinese. Scrofa scrofa is the common wild boar of Europe, Asia and North Africa; it was domesticated independently. The long-bodied, snub-nosed, fat "porker" was bred from a fortunate mutation; nothing similar ever existed in the wild state.

In the Pleistocene the wild aurochs was widely distributed over Europe, northern Africa and Asia. It was a huge animal with very long horns; but judging from an excellent late Paleolithic engraving discovered in a cave of the Dordogne in France, there seems to have existed a smaller species much more like our modern cattle. It is possible that this species, or the result of its interbreeding with the aurochs, yielded the varieties that were domesticated about 4000 B.C. The still smaller, humped zebu cattle are, apart from the water buffalo, the only bovines which thrive in the tropics. They were probably domesticated in India from the indigenous Pleistocene *Bos nomadicus*. The earliest evidence of the zebu's domestication dates back to the Indian Bronze Age civilizations of 2500–1500 B.C., but of course it may have taken place much earlier, though the zebu did not spread over the African continent until about 1000 B.C.

Among primitive people the belief is still widely held that it is very unhealthy for an adult to drink cow's milk. Moreover, before high-yielding cows were bred by a long process of careful selection, most of the milk was needed to rear a healthy calf. In a hot climate, and without any knowledge of bacteriology, dairy products could not be preserved except in the form of *ghee*. Ghee is butter that has been heated until all the water is driven off, leaving a pure liquid fat that does not become rancid. Therefore it

is not surprising that the habitual drinking of milk came
late and may have started on a large and general scale with
the Buddhistic vegetarians. The utilization of curds followed; but the making of butter and cheese were even
later developments.

In Africa, the nomadic Masai are great cattle-breeders
and drink the blood rather than the milk of their animals,
regularly tapping it from the jugular vein. With indisputable logic, they claim that they can thereby live off bulls
and cows without having to slaughter the former for food.
However, there is probably an added reason for this nutritional custom. When man drinks cow's or goat's milk his
digestive system requires about an equal amount of water
to break up the coagulum which forms in his stomach,
Blood, on the other hand, can be digested without additional water; and as droughts are common in the Masai
country, this factor may have been of importance in their
preferring blood to milk.

Though goats, pigs, sheep and cattle were by far the
most important Neolithic domestications, many other animals were brought under human control. The Central
Americans domesticated the llama, the alpaca and the
vicuña, all relations of the camel; and in northern Europe
the Lapps tamed the reindeer. The ass and the onager
were used at an early date as pack animals, and as early as
3000 B.C. they were used for pulling wheeled carts in
Mesopotamia. The horse was domesticated in northwest
Asia and from there spread into Europe during the Bronze
Age, about 2000 B.C.

The dromedary or Arabian camel was domesticated at
an early but uncertain date. It is now unknown in the wild
state, possibly because it is a rather dull and easily tamed
animal and so extraordinarily useful in the desert. Once
the knack of domesticating it had been acquired, every
wild specimen was pressed into service as soon as it was

encountered. The double-humped Bactrian camel is indigenous to Central Asia, but it is fairly certain from fossil evidence that both species originated in North America and from there spread over the Old World, leaving behind their closest relations the llamas, alpacas and vicuñas.

During the second millennium B.C. the Indians learned to domesticate their elephants, a much greater achievement than taming camels. Elephants were already in general use when Alexander the Great invaded India. The African elephant was also tamed, but the first clear evidence of this domestication dates back to Ptolemaic times. Elephants were captured and tamed in the Nile Valley, though it was probably not the large bush elephant of East Africa, but a smaller variety, now extinct, that lived in the forests of North Africa and along the Atlantic coast. This is suggested by the relative size of the animals and their riders as represented on old Egyptian seals. Altogether, the ancient Egyptians seem to have been enthusiastic domesticators, for there is evidence to suggest that they tried their luck, albeit unsuccessfully, with antelopes, gazelles, monkeys, and even hyenas.

From a nutritional point of view the domestication of poultry is most important; but unfortunately we know very little about it, except that it started independently in many parts of the world. Local species were gradually brought under human control to supply the demand for birds and eggs for which most primates have always had a special craving. In Central America the turkey was certainly a most important source of animal food.

The domestication of animals is an astounding intellectual feat that followed closely upon the beginnings of agriculture. It probably started with the brilliant idea that instead of hunting, killing, and immediately eating the wild animals that raided Neolithic man's precious crops, it would be wiser to catch them alive, keep them in stockades, feed them, and eventually control their breeding. As was the case with agriculture, this notion required a full stomach, leisure for deep cogitation, and the overcoming of the ingrained "kill-and-eat" instinct before the barriers of ridicule and bitter opposition could be broken.

Man probably learned the connection between copulation and pregnancy from his animals, and from them may have suspected the inevitability of death, though until quite recently there still existed tribes living on a Paleolithic level of culture who knew nothing of these facts of life.

By killing and eating the wildest and most troublesome bulls, rams, and boars and sparing the docile ones, the various domestic breeds gradually became tamer and more manageable. But only after the mechanism of procreation was understood could selective breeding be initiated; and this led to the incredible number of man-made variations from which we can now choose our domestic animals.

TRANSPORT

The earliest form of transportation was by river: on rafts made of logs, as on the Congo; on bundles of papyrus as on the Nile; or on inflated skins stretched on a wicker-work frame as in Mesopotamia, where neither reeds nor trees could be found along the banks of the Tigris and Euphrates. Such craft can hardly have been seaworthy, but there is very early evidence of boats made by stretching skins over a wooden framework, much like the kayak used by male Eskimos or the umiak, which their women use. It is possible that such craft were used on the open sea between the Italian mainland and the Aeolean islands to transport the volcanic obsidian so valuable for making sharp stone implements. It is also known that there was an early trade in stone axe blades across the Irish Sea.

It is often assumed that the first dugouts could only have been made after man had learned how to manufacture highly finished stone tools, yet it is possible to make a good canoe by the careful use of fire applied to a large log. The charred wood can easily be removed with relatively primitive implements, so that quite seaworthy craft may be of much older date. Indeed, a Mesolithic example was unearthed near Perth. Neolithic canoes made of oak logs have been found in Scandinavia, Britain, Germany, and Switzerland, which suggests that they were not a recent invention even in Neolithic times. From our point of view, seafaring is important because it added deep-sea fish to the human diet, which, as far as fish was concerned, had been confined to the yield of rivers, lakes, and coastal waters. In fact, in Denmark the bones of cod, plaice and dogfish have been found in the middens of Neolithic hunter-fishers.

In Scandinavia sledges dragged by dogs or men were already in use in Neolithic times and were employed not only on snowfields but also on the rich spring grass and on marshland. The wheel was invented much later—we do not know exactly when or where—and was subsequently used for transport. In those Neolithic days there can have been little inducement to increase the speed of moving from place to place, and roads, of course, had not yet been thought of. Again we feel an aura of genius when we picture some Neolithic tinker conceiving the seemingly crazy idea of fitting two potter's wheels on an axle, tipping them on their rims, and fixing this contraption under a sledge. His contemporaries must have marveled and laughed, just as the good townsfolk did when the first "horseless carriages" appeared on the streets, just over half a century ago. Yet without this Neolithic extravaganza there would have been no roads and no machines. Our first evidence of a wheel dates back to 1900 B.C., but the invention was certainly made much earlier. In Europe wheels seem to have been rare until the Bronze Age (about 500 B.C.), but being made entirely of wood, they can have been preserved only under particularly lucky circumstances.

CONTAINERS

The early agriculturists were semi-nomadic. After they had cleared the ground, sown their crop, and harvested it, they moved on. Only after they learned to revive the fertility of the soil by turning it over—ploughing the earth, even if only superficially with a stag's antler or a forked branch—did they become permanently settled, giving rise to urban civilization. Before that time, man used leather bags, gourds, and wickerwork covered with hides or besmeared with clay to transport his harvest and the precious seed to the next site.

In the days before the invention of pottery man could, by various cumbersome artifices, bring water to boil to cook his food. But the enormous advantages of a manufactured gadget that could be filled with water and placed directly upon the fire may have been a subject of science fiction imagining among advanced Neolithic thinkers. They may have experimented with hard wood, coconut shells, ostrich egg shells, skulls, or hides; but they seem to have decided that stone was, after all, the most promising material. And so with admirable industry and patience they set about making stone bowls, chiseling and polishing until the walls became thinner and thinner. They already had mortars and pestles which they used to pound roots, nuts, grain, and the pigments they used for their paintings. It was from these that they made deeper and finer bowls and in this work they achieved an astounding skill. They had as little inkling of the marvelous properties of burned clay as we had of plastics a hundred years ago.

At this point genius again intervened. Thousands of times wicker baskets, caked with clay to make them airtight for storing grain, must have accidentally burned in the camp fire. The woodwork burned away, but the clay retained its shape and became stone hard, watertight, and brittle. These earliest potsherds were thoughtlessly thrown away until someone had the brilliant idea of fashioning a pot of clay without the wickerwork, drying this useless vessel in the sun, and then deliberately firing it. It required years and possibly lifetimes of persistent experimentation with clay mixtures, kilns and fuels before really good results were achieved; but with this first idea, pottery was born.

The first Neolithic potters made their earthenware by building up spiraling coils of clay on a slab of stone and then smoothing them over. Later an assistant provided a rotary movement to the base while the master was at work. Later still, the assistant's work was made smoother, faster, and easier by some intellectual giant who conceived the revolutionary idea of a wheel and axle. Later an equally clever craftsman invented the footwheel which made the assistant superfluous. All these events must have been wildly exciting and must have spread rapidly from settlement to settlement.

REGULAR MEALS AND OBESITY

We are not concerned here with many other Neolithic achievements which erupted in a bewildering variety (much as scientific progress in our own day). Spinning and weaving were discovered, houses were built and decorated, and burial rites—of which the Neanderthalers had already evolved rudiments—were vastly elaborated. Religions became more complex and the movements of stars and planets were watched; this led to the reckoning of time in years and seasons with the beginnings of mathematics, writing, and record keeping. What is important for our topic is that with roasting, baking, boiling, and smoking, man became mainly an eater of cooked food and henceforth depended heavily upon his kitchen.

The discovery of metal and metallurgy, which had such a profound influence on almost every other human activity, did not incisively affect feeding until the recent industrialization of food production. It brought better weapons, axes, knives, and fish hooks. There followed spoons and forks, cauldrons and the chains that held them, pans, skillets, and small iron stoves in which charcoal could be burned and carried. But all this kitchenware brought no radical change in diet.

However the Neolithic age did bring one other innovation which has profoundly influenced all subsequent human feeding, and that is the institution of regular meals. Before the professional exercise of crafts, agriculture, and especially animal husbandry forced man into some sort of daily schedule, feeding was entirely determined by hunger, regardless of the time of day or night. Moreover, no more was eaten at a time than was necessary to still the pangs of hunger. In fact, the structure of the human intestinal tract is organized to deal most efficiently with frequent snacks, rather than with a sudden influx of food on two or three occasions in the course of twenty-four hours.

Regular meals that could be prepared at certain hours of the day simplified the kitchen routine and left the womenfolk time for other chores such as fetching water, scrubbing pots (which they did with ashes), helping in the fields, and feeding and milking the domestic animals. Infants were of course breast-fed until they had to make room at the font for the next arrival, and sometimes they were suckled even after the birth of a competitor, as is still quite common in the Far East. Infants were carried by the mother wherever she went, and perhaps the horrible practice of swaddling originated thus: it made the parcel handier and protected the mother from soiling by her infant's excreta.

The Neolithic institution of meals contributed heavily to modern man's affliction with obesity. I have dealt with this problem at some length in my book *Man's Presumptuous Brain;* so it may here suffice to say that when many hours of fasting are interspersed between meals, there develops a tendency to eat more at each meal than the body requires at that moment. This surplus fuel is stored by the body in the form of fat, which is not fully consumed by the time the next meal is due. It has rightly been pointed out that obesity would be a less serious problem if man would revert to eating frequent snacks instead of a few heavy meals. However, the way our lives are organized there seems to be little hope of this ever coming about.

There are two other factors responsible in some measure for the scourge of obesity, and they too date back to the Neolithic age. The first is the rapid increase in the consumption of cooked—particularly boiled—food as against raw food. The human intestine digests and assimilates cooked and refined food such as polished rice, finely milled white wheat flour, peeled potatoes, boiled vegetables, etc., far more rapidly than their raw and natural equivalents. The result is that shortly after a meal our system is quickly flooded with more nutriment than it can make use of at the time. The surplus goes into abnormal fat deposits which are no longer metabolically available to the body, so that in spite of adequate reserves, the obese patient feels ravenously hungry by the time the next meal is due and must therefore again overeat. Once this vicious cycle has been established it is almost impossible to stop it by eating less.

The second factor that has contributed to the prevalence of obesity is a genetic one. From Neolithic times to our day there has been a sexual selection favoring an inherited tendency toward overweight. In the marriage market a plump girl has almost universally had a better chance than a skinny one. This is so not only for erotic reasons, but also because fat became a symbol of health and wealth and thus an important consideration wherever the family made the choice of the partner. Before Neolithic times, individual property hardly existed; but when families began to own houses, herds, and arable land, matchmaking was largely subjected to economic considerations and expediency, causing the trend to overweight to spread.

THE GARDEN OF EDEN

In a few beautiful words the Bible tells the story of the Neolithic revolution. In Paleolithic Eden man was indeed "innocent" of himself, his destiny to die, and the causal connection between sex and birth. As in the Bible, it was surely woman who unraveled the latter mystery. She learned through her deep natural interest in copulation and delivery among the domestic animals she tended, (rather than from the undomesticated snake) .

It is interesting that in the Revised Oxford translation of the Bible, Genesis IV, verse 14, runs as follows: "And the Lord God said unto the serpent, Because thou hast done this thou art cursed above all *cattle* and above every beast in the field; upon thy belly shalt thou go, and dust shalt thou eat all the days of thy life." This suggests that before the curse was invoked the tempter had legs; nor would it be entirely out of the female character if Eve had had misgivings about telling Adam the whole truth of how she made her awful discovery and unjustly blamed that oldest enemy of tree-living primates, the tree serpent.

"And to Adam the Lord God said: Thou shalt eat of it (the ground) all the days of thy life. In the sweat of thy face thou shalt eat bread till thou return to the ground. Unto Adam and his wife did the Lord God make coats of skin and clothed them. The Lord God sent him forth from the Garden of Eden to till the ground."

Feeding in Historic Times

NEOLITHIC and even Paleolithic and Mesolithic modes of feeding persisted in many parts of the world among millions of men who continued to live on these primitive levels of culture almost to our day. Elsewhere three main factors, religion, transport and urbanization influenced the development of dietary patterns. Religions imposed rules and prohibitions which differed from primitive taboos in that they were applied to all, and for all times. Transport, trade, and travel added outlandish crops, foods, and spices to the local diets. Urbanization produced merchants who bought and sold grain to those who could no longer grow their own, and often the governing authority controlled its storage and distribution. Butchers, bakers, grocers, fuel vendors, and dealers in spices, oils, and wines began to ply their trades.

Urban populations ceased to hunt and fish for themselves and the number of cattle, sheep, goats, pigs, and poultry kept by each family suffered a rapid decline. For the first time there appeared urban families that had no claim to any land and could still make a living as artisans, craftsmen, merchants, scribes, priests and mercenaries. Whereas formerly food was eaten as it was hunted, fished, and gathered, grain and oil were now stored from one harvest to the next. Meat and fish were preserved by salting, smoking—a process probably as old as the domestication of fire—and sun drying. Beans, peas, and lentils were also dried. Fruit was similarly treated or preserved in honey.

Wherever men ceased to produce their own food, standard diets developed, with a strong tendency to revert to vegetable food, which by reckoning based on its caloric value became much cheaper than meat. Thus staple foods were developed such as rice in tropical and sub-tropical Asia, the millets in Africa, wheat in the temperate zones, and oats in the North. It was only in post-Columbian times that maize, potatoes, and groundnuts started their spectacular success in the Old World. The potato largely replaced oats in the North; and maize became a strong competitor of wheat and millet. The groundnut, which will grow on the poorest soil enriching it in the process, easily outdid the coconut and the palm nut as a tropical source of oil, while the sunflower was added to soya beans, olives and linseed as a source of vegetable oil in the southern temperate zones. In the North, butter and animal fats continued to be the mainstay of nutritional fat, as most oil-yielding plants need a warm climate. In a cool climate, butter, particularly when salted, can be kept fresh in caves and cellars all the year round.

We will now discuss some of the dietary peculiarities which various civilizations evolved.

CHINA

The Chinese have a saying that anything which lives is edible, provided you know how to cook it. The maxim made them the most sophisticated master-cooks in the world. They evolved a finer art out of delicately stimulating the senses of taste, smell, and oral touch, and have more diligently explored what nature has to offer these senses than any other people.

Owing to this adventurous culinary attitude and a complete absence of nutritional bias, their skill enabled them to make delicacies out of eggs that have undergone a slow process of decomposition after being buried for years in a special kind of clay. They also used sharks' fins, gelatinous nests of cliff-swallows, rats, chow puppies, snakes, various insects, and a long list of other items which would make Western man shudder if they appeared on his table. They also knew the exact point at which cooked vegetables cease to taste raw and still retain a certain fresh crispness.

With their rice bowls, chopsticks and short-handled porcelain spoons the Chinese are delicate feeders. It is the cook's business to see that nothing that needs to be cut, torn or bitten off is served. The morsel is the biggest unit permissible and it must be edible in its entirety. There must be no bones, no hard gristle, no tendons and in vegetables no woody parts. In Chinese feeding there is no such thing as gnawing a drumstick or spitting pips.

Obviously not all Chinese are gourmets and only a small, well-to-do minority can afford to whet its appetite with gastronomic extravaganzas. The common man is content if he can get enough to fill his belly with rice, bean curds, noodles, vegetables in season and such slivers of poultry, fish, prawns, or pork as his means permit.

Wherever rice is eaten it is polished, a process whereby the cuticle, rich in proteins and vitamins, is removed. This polishing renders the grain white, more insipid, and consisting almost entirely of pure starch. It is an extraordinary fact that man always tries to make his staple food as neutral to taste as possible, and preferably white. Thus white flour is appreciated more than whole-grain flour, and this is why nutritious potato peel is discarded and why pears and apples are peeled. It is hard to say whether this nutritional sacrifice is made for an ostentatious concern with appearances, or for the purpose of keeping the palate from growing weary of a food with a particular flavor that is eaten in large quantities twice a day for a lifetime.

Of all cereals rice seems to stimulate the appetite least. This is possibly why all rice-eaters evoke a satisfactory flow of gastric digestive juices by using highly flavored condiments containing strong peppers or, in China, the pungent soybean sauce. However, the habitual use of hot spices is not confined to rice-eaters. It is normal in all hot countries, and for this there may be two reasons. One is that the food eaten tends to be monotonous, lacking surprise and variety. Secondly, the loss of chlorine through strong perspiration at high environmental temperatures is considerable, so that the stomach may need powerful stimulation to produce an adequate amount of hydrochloric acid, the most important of all digestive juices.

The soybean sauce used in China is prepared from the residue which remains after the oil has been extracted from the bean. It has a very strong flavor similar to that of yeast and is rich in high-grade proteins and the vitamin B complex, just the nutritional factors which polishing removes from the rice grain.

Perhaps China's most important contribution towards stimulating the taste buds and the nervous system of man all the world over is the introduction of tea, but of this we shall have more to say later.

INDIA

Indians are scrupulously clean eaters. No orthodox Hindu would think of having a meal before he had washed his body and donned a spotlessly clean, thin, cotton loin-cloth known as a *dhoti*. He eats alone while the womenfolk serve him. He sits cross-legged on the floor and has before him a large metal platter on which little metal cups of vegetables, curries, spices and chutneys are placed round the edge of a large mound of gleaming rice. He eats with his hands, using only the thumb and the first two fingers of the right hand with which he deftly prepares a mouthful. This he flicks into his mouth with a quick jerk of his thumb, never wetting his fingers with saliva. After the meal the mouth is at once rinsed and the soiled hand is washed in running water poured from a ewer into a basin. Saliva is always considered polluting and therefore when two Hindus share a cigarette, they do not pass it from mouth to mouth. It is held between two fingers of the closely cupped hands, and the smoke is inhaled between the two thumbs that lie next to each other.

In the northern Sind Plain the staple food is wheat. It is eaten unleavened in flat pancakes called *chappaties* which are made of unrefined, often home-milled flour with water and a sprinkling of the melted butter known as *ghee*. Dhal and other pulses (seeds) are regularly eaten, also sweetmeats prepared from honey, raw cane sugar, nuts and *ghee*. The sweets are usually flavored with rosewater and other essences and often decorated with fine silver or gold leaf, which is eaten. Milk, chiefly water-buffalo milk, is taken fresh or boiled with very strong sweetened tea, or it is eaten as curds. Cheeses are practically unknown.

An almost universal habit is the chewing of *pan-sopari* which stimulates a strong salivation and turns the saliva brick-red, staining lips, gums and teeth. It serves much the same purpose as chewing gum, except that it is nutritionally much more valuable, owing to its vitamin B and C content. *Pan-sopari* is prepared by taking a fresh, carefully washed leaf of the betel vine (a close relation of the peppers) and spreading slaked lime, the so called *chunam*, over its surface. With an instrument rather like a nut-cracker, except that one side has a sharp blade, a little pile of slivers is cut from an areca-nut onto the prepared leaf. It is confusing that the areca-nut, the seed of a graceful palm, is also called a betel-nut, though botanically it has nothing whatever to do with the betel vine.

In an unsophisticated *pan-sopari* the leaf is folded into a neat little parcel round the slivers of nut and is then ready for chewing. Often, however, various spices or to-bacco are added to these ingredients; the parcel may be sealed with a clove imported from the Island of Zanzibar, and on festive occasions it may be covered with gold leaf. The large number of *pan-soparis* that some people con-sume in a day, and the deftness with which they prepare their masticatory delight are equally astounding.

Brahmins and Buddhists are strict vegetarians, in the sense that the only food of animal origin they eat is milk and its derivates, unless one includes honey in this cate-gory. Though a rice-eater must have the carnivorous sup-plement of milk in large quantities in order to stay healthy, I have, in India, met a few elderly vegetarians in reasonably good health who drank no milk; they lived mainly on groundnuts, raw cane sugar, honey, fruits, vegetables, pulses, and fermenting palm sap. However such diets are rare oddities and would certainly not do for a growing child.

When refrigerated transport of milk was introduced some twenty-five years ago, the peasants in the country surrounding the towns stopped walking their cows and buffaloes from door to door and milking them in front of their clients. They also began to suffer from severe malnutrition, because it was so profitable to sell all the milk they produced that they severely cut down their own consumption. They then went to the cities for expensive medical consultations and the prescription of equally expensive medicines for disorders which were entirely due to a lack of animal protein. The disorders cleared up as soon as they were advised to drink more of the milk their cows produced instead of selling it all.

With an ample intake of milk and plenty of nuts and pulses, the Indian vegetarian diet is nutritionally quite satisfactory, particularly if buffalo and goat's milk are used. Owing to the buffalo's much larger yield of milk with a very high fat content, it is economically feasible to give these animals supplementary feeds such as cottonseed and groundnut cake. These residues are left after the oil has been expelled and are highly nutritious in vitamins and proteins. The cow, on the other hand, is sacred and is not purposefully bred by eliminating productively worthless animals, with the result that the yield of milk is quantitatively and qualitatively very poor. Great efforts are being made by the Indian government to correct this situation, but though there are now a large number of model dairies run on the most modern lines, progress is slow and handicapped by the special position held by the cow in Indian beliefs. It is still impossible to slaughter inferior animals, particularly as the meat cannot be sold. Not only Brahmins, but even non-vegetarian Hindus of any caste would refuse to touch it. The orthodox do not even wear shoes or sandals made of cow's hide.

The meat-eating Hindus add mutton, goat, chicken, eggs, and—along the coast—fish to their staple diet. They will eat wild boar, but not domestic pig, because these are almost exclusively reared and eaten by Untouchables. Domestic pigs that roam in the villages are known to eat excrement. For both these reasons they are considered tainted and unclean. It does not appear to bother anyone that the wild boar and his mate presumably have similarly unsavory habits.

The Muslim population, on the other hand, will eat no pork of any kind and can get beef only where Mohammedans are in an overwhelming majority; living in a Hindu community they are confined to sheep, goats, and poultry. So strong are these feelings that in many of the old Native States it was impossible for European residents openly to import corned beef, and those of us who wanted even such a humble change from the eternal goat and chicken had to smuggle it in with carefully thought-out stratagems. In many parts of India wild peacocks are abundant and the pea-hen is just as good eating as turkey; but peafowl are sacred, and woe betide the fowler who bags one for the pot.

In India there are wandering tribes who specialize in ridding houses, gardens, and plantations of the enormous rat-like burrowing bandicoots. They not only catch and kill them but also eat and evidently enjoy the fruits of their labors. Other tribes professionally catch the civet cats that make themselves at home under the roofs of old country houses and barns. For these men too their catch is edible. In Ceylon, the large monitor lizards are considered a delicacy. When they are caught, their tails are thrust into their throats and the ring thus formed is happily carried home from the jungle.

For a research project I once bred rabbits and guinea pigs at the country place far out in the wilds where we spent our week-ends. The rabbits never seemed to get ahead, owing to a heavy mortality during the weekdays when we were not there, while the guinea pigs thrived prodigiously. One day I thought I would have this out with the servants, local people of the jungle, who would never lie to my face. I told them that I could understand that a fat rabbit could be too tempting to resist, but that I could not understand why they spared the guinea pigs. Laughing shyly, they confessed the whole sordid truth. Yes, they had eaten some rabbits, but only those that looked as if they were going to die anyhow. They had never seen a guinea pig before, so they had called a council of "five wise men" to decide whether the guinea pigs were edible. After due deliberation and a bit of zoological freewheeling the council declared them to be small dogs and as such unfit for human consumption.

In some parts of India, the Deccan plateau for instance, there is a common nutritional disease of which children die at the age of about two years. The signs, symptoms and the clinical course are identical with the alcoholic cirrhosis of the liver with which we are familiar, except that it occurs early in life and is not associated with alcoholic indulgence. The fact that it so closely resembles alcoholic cirrhosis suggests that the latter condition is not caused by the alcohol as such, but rather by the nutritional deficiencies to which alcoholics are liable and which are caused by alcoholic gastritis, carelessness in feeding, or poverty. In fact, it has recently been shown that, together with a satisfactory dietary regimen and in the absence of gastritis, alcohol can be given to patients suffering from cirrhosis without any untoward consequences.

Indigent rice-eaters are generally lean in spite of the high caloric intake furnished by oil, rice and sugar of which they eat very large quantities. This seems to have engendered the entirely false belief still held in many quarters, even among the medical profession, that rice is not fattening. The leanness of poor habitual rice-eaters is entirely due to a lack of high-grade protein in their diet, and without this protein, the body cannot build fatty tissue. The addition of a small amount of high-grade protein to a poor rice-eater's diet is soon followed by an increase in weight, although the caloric value of the added meat is negligible.

In countries with a very ancient civilization and thousands of years of hygienic habit formation, inducing or advocating changes in age-old dietary patterns may wreak nutritional havoc. We have seen how this happened in Nauru; but it is also observed when laborers of peasant stock move into the cities. There they confine themselves to a few staple foods and give up all the occasional snacks and delicacies they have regularly obtained from their farms or the nearby jungle. Gradually they get weaker and paler and develop digestive disorders before they finally decide to take a holiday on their farm. There they work even harder than in the cities, yet when they return after a couple of weeks their health has improved most surprisingly. As such Indians take their wives and children with them when they move to the city, and as they all show a dramatic change for the better after such a visit to their home, this has nothing to do with poor working conditions; it is very largely nutritional.

When old dietary habits are changed because doctors impose too many restrictions, when the high spicing of tropical food is discouraged or the abstention from *pan-sopari* is advocated on aesthetic grounds, malnutrition is all too often the result. This is something non-Indian well-wishers should bear in mind. Habits which seem strange and even disgusting to us may be of quite unexpected importance within the framework of an old established dietary pattern.

ANCIENT GREECE

According to the historian Will Durant, the nutritional habits of the ancient Greeks were frugal. In historic times Greece has always been an agriculturally poor country as far as growing grain is concerned. The Greeks soon came to depend heavily on imported cereals for which they paid with their surplus of wine and olive oil. This export and import was the basic factor in the rapid growth of the Greek colonial empire and the need for a large and powerful fleet.

In the cultivation of figs the Greeks reached a high degree of perfection, particularly after they learned from the East the secret of hanging branches of the wild goatfig, *Caprificus,* into the boughs of the female cultivated tree. This process, known as caprification, induces the gallwasps which are responsible for the pollination to do a better job and thereby increase the yield. In ancient Greece the fig was nutritionally so important that its export was strictly forbidden. Cereals, olive oil, grapes and figs thus became staple foods.

The locally grown grain and most vegetables had to be harvested in May before the torrid and rainless summer put an end to agricultural productivity. Owing to this long and arid summer, cattle rearing as a source of meat was hardly attempted. Horses were bred for racing, sheep for wool, goats for milk, asses, mules, cows and oxen for transport. Pigs and poultry were the chief animal foods, though among the poor meat was a great luxury. Most of the fish caught was sun-dried or salted and was then relatively cheap. Only the rich could afford fresh fish and such delicacies as shark meat or eels. In this as yet sugarless world bees were kept in large numbers.

Eggs, beans, peas, lentils, cabbage, lettuce, onions, and garlic were eaten with bread and oil. Potatoes, tomatoes, oranges and lemons were of course still unknown; and, apart from figs and grapes, there were hardly any other fruits that could be profitably grown in the Greek climate. Nuts were, however, plentiful. Salt was made in salt-pans from sea water and traded into the interior for slaves; hence the expression "a man is worth his salt." Bread and cakes were seldom baked at home. They were bought at market stalls or from women who peddled them in the streets. They were often flavored with cheese made from goats' milk or sweetened with honey. The cheese cakes were so popular that several classic treatises on their preparation are known to us.

Snow and ice were brought from the mountains and kept in deep caves or cellars to cool the wine in summer. Beer was known but despised, as is usual in wine-growing countries. Even down to our day the food of poor Greeks is much the same as it was in Classical days, except for such additions as the citrus fruits, tea, coffee, sugar, and some outlandish spices. The legendary, Homeric banquets of yore were history even to the ancients.

The Romans

The Chinese had made a fine art out of cookery long before the Romans achieved sufficient wealth and refinement to indulge in such luxuries, but within the boundaries of Western civilization the credit for introducing extravagant sophistication into the kitchen must go to the Romans. Basically their food was much like that of the Greeks, but they did have rather more latitude, because the Italian peninsula is much more fertile than Greece.

With the enormous expansion of their empire and the influx of men and slaves who had new skills, Roman feeding rapidly improved in quality and diversity. It also seems probable that the early Romans, still rude and barbaric, learned much of the art of living from the highly artistic and widely seafaring Etruscans who surrounded them and whose cultured women they robbed and raped. Though far less crudely dynamic than the Romans, the Etruscans lived refined and cultured lives and, as the Romans mixed with them and then exterminated them, much of Etruscan culture outlived its originators as an early stimulant to Roman civilization. Indeed, it may have outlived the ancient Romans themselves in the artistry, gaiety, charm and *joie-de-vivre* of the modern Italians.

When the Romans feasted they lay on couches, a habit which may have existed among rich Egyptians but does not seem to have caught on elsewhere. Awkward for eating as this prone position may have been, it seems to have encouraged convivial conversation, amorous sport, and drunkenness as their writers amply testify. It is only of the Romans that we know that they did not mind vomiting in order to make room for further delicacies. They also en-

joyed watching lions kill and devour human beings and
they built beautiful roads deep into the African continent
to keep up, among other things, a steady supply of wild
beasts. Apart from such oddities and crudities, the Romans
contributed little that was new or of lasting value toward
human feeding until their modern descendants turned the
old Chinese noodles into spaghetti, fettucini, macaroni,
and their myriad variations.

THE JEWS

Complicated systems of tribal, familial and individual
taboos reach far back into Paleolithic times, but the Israel-
ites, who were the first monotheists, were also the first to
lay down seemingly arbitrary rules about which food was
"clean" and which was "unclean"—and therefore forbidden to the extent that even touching the carcass of an
"unclean" animal was considered a pollution lasting until
sunset.

It has been said that these food laws, as laid down in
the Old Testament (Leviticus XI; Deuteronomy XII,
XLV, and elsewhere), were motivated by hygienic considerations. I have heard it said that placing pork on the
unclean list is a wise measure against the dangerous disease
of trichinosis which man can acquire by eating raw pork
infested with the worm trichina. This happy contention
overlooks the fact that trichinosis hardly exists in the East
and that these early Jews cannot possibly have connected
clinical symptoms—appearing several weeks after eating
the infested pork—with the often-fatal meal, even if trichinosis existed among them. It was only in 1835 that the
great British physician, Sir James Paget, discovered the

tiny parasite; and although epidemic outbreaks had raged through northern Europe for centuries, the causal connection between the worm and the disease was only discovered in 1860 by Friedrich von Zenker. The disease has now all but disappeared in these northern countries, owing to the compulsory microscopic check of all pork by a qualified veterinary surgeon. Yet elsewhere hundreds of millions of people, in India, China, and Indonesia for instance, continue to eat pork that has never been checked without untoward results.

It seems much more likely that the pig's muck-grubbing and entirely omnivorous habits made its flesh seem unclean to the fastidious, in spite of the fact that from a nutritional point of view its meat is unsurpassed. If one thinks back to the time when the Jews set themselves apart from the general Semitic stock from which they arose, and then reads the lists of what they may and may not eat, one cannot avoid the impression that a good deal of snobbery went into the making of these decisions. Only the very best and presumably the most expensive animal food was allowed, while humbler fare such as camel meat, hare, rabbit, and all seafood other than fishes with fins and scales, were forbidden as unclean. Of particular interest in connection with our previous discussions is that locusts, grasshoppers, and beetles (their larvae) are expressly stated to be clean and edible. Thus if an orthodox Hebrew washes his hands with soap made of whale oil, he becomes unclean instead of clean. In Dutch slang as used in Amsterdam, peanuts are jokingly called *joden garnaaltjes* which means: shrimps for Jews.

To qualify for the Jewish kitchen, animals must be cloven-hoofed and chew the cud, a rule which greatly encouraged animal husbandry. All animals that have paws, bats, birds of prey, amphibians, and reptiles are forbidden; so no frogs' legs and no turtle soup may be eaten;   and though insects are permissible, snails are not. Blood of slaughtered animals is unclean and must be "spilled on the ground." The sciatic nerve must be removed from the hind legs (Genesis XXXII, 32) and flesh must not be cooked in milk (Exodus XXIII, 19).

Eating fish instead of meat as a form of fasting is of Jewish origin and the unleavened bread eaten at Passover and still normally eaten in the Far East, is a relic of the old days when the Jews normally ate such bread. Jewish religious, moral, and dietary laws profoundly influenced both Christianity and Islam. How pervasive this dietary influence still is, throughout the patterns of Western man's feeding, becomes very clear when we compare them with Chinese, Indian, or African attitudes toward food.

In order to feed the herds of domestic animals on which they chiefly lived, the Jews needed to develop that high agricultural skill under adverse climatic and geological conditions, which they have again so brilliantly demonstrated in modern Israel. This enabled them to make a very early change from nomadic to urban life and civilization of which the oldest ruins of Jericho bear ample witness.

We shall now briefly discuss the origins of three universally used items of diet; namely tea, coffee, and chocolate.

TEA

The true origin of tea is unknown, but legends abound. According to one version, its discovery is attributed to the Chinese Emperor Shên-nung, about 2737 B.C.;

but as the Chinese trace all agricultural and medical knowledge to this outstanding ruler, the inclusion of tea among his evidently countless accomplishments is not too convincing.

Another tradition has it that tea originally came from India, imported by Buddhist monks on mission bent, and more specifically by one Bodhidharma under rather peculiar circumstances in the year A.D. 543. This ascetic rashly made a vow that he would contemplate the virtues of Buddha for nine consecutive years without sleep. However, after only three years he fell asleep. On awakening, he became so angry with himself that he cut off his eyelids and threw them on the ground beside him. This heroic mutilation permitted him to indulge in uninterrupted meditation for another five years before he again began to feel unbearably drowsy. But meanwhile, a shrub had grown by his side on the spot where he had thrown his eyelids and its leaves had the shape of his offending palpebrae. Of these leaves he ate, became immediately wide awake, and was thus able to keep himself in this blissful state for the remaining year of devotions.

We know from Arab sources that tea was used in China in the ninth century and at about that time it was introduced to Japan. Tea first came to England from Java in 1650, but this source stopped in 1686 when the British were driven out of the island by the Dutch. At first tea cost the enormous sum of £6 to £10 per pound, but already in the year 1660 it was being offered by one Thomas Garway of London at 15 to 50 shillings per pound; and it was in this year that Samuel Pepys made its acquaintance.

The tea was bought by the East India Company from Chinese junks that brought it to Madras and Surat, and only very much later was it obtained directly from China. At the close of the eighteenth century the English were already consuming about two pounds per head per annum, and so the almost insurmountable difficulties in trading with China induced the East India Company to try growing tea in the territories it controlled. In 1834 Captain Francis Jenkins proved that genuine tea grew wild in Upper Assam, further support for the view that the use of tea started in India and then fell into disuse. It was, therefore, decided by Lord William Bentnick to start the cultivation of tea in Assam. However, in 1835 the monopoly of the East India Company was abolished and from then on the cultivation of tea spread rapidly to Indonesia, Ceylon, and Africa and it was then not long before tea imported directly from China became freely available.

There are many varieties of the shrub and many ways of preparing the beverage. In India tea leaves with a little water and plenty of rich buffalo milk and sugar are all boiled together. The Dutch still boil a highly concentrated extract which they then dilute in the cup with water, milk, and sugar to taste. In the Himalayan foothills right up into Tibet, tea is carried in the form of hard bricks by caravans of yaks and is mixed with various spices and perfumes. Chinese tea is—or ought to be—drunk without milk or sugar, and it is often perfumed with jasmine blossoms. In Japan tea-drinking has developed into a complicated ritual, and the Russians have their *samovar*. Today most of the tea consumed is black, having been subjected to a process of fermentation; in China the leaves are merely dried and make a pale-greenish tea.

The New World Indians had a tea of their own from very ancient times, the so-called *maté* or Paraguay tea. It is prepared from the leaves, and occasionally the buds, of an ilex, an evergreen belonging to the same genus as holly. In the wild it grows into a tree, but when cultivated it remains an evergreen shrub. Jesuit missionaries were the first to start its cultivation, and thus produced a tea far superior to that made with the wild-growing leaves. The leaves are picked only every two or three years and are heat-dried in a process quite similar to the making of China tea. *Maté* is extensively consumed in Paraguay and Southern Brazil, but has, in spite of many efforts, never found favor in the rest of the world. It contains very little caffein and is prepared in a small silver-mounted calabash, a hollowed gourd, or pumpkin. Sugar and a little water are put into the calabash, the tea is added, and the vessel filled with hot water or milk. It is then sucked up through a *bombilla*—a reed or metal tube, about six inches long, that has a bulb of extremely fine basketwork or of metal with tiny holes at the lower end to prevent the crushed leaves from reaching the mouth. Burnt sugar or lemon juice are sometimes added instead of milk.

COFFEE

The coffee plant is indigenous to Abyssinia, but its cultivation and use spread outward from southern Arabia. Various wild coffee species, of which about 25 are known, occur in parts of Africa. They have been found on the shores of the Victoria Nayansa Lake, in Mozambique, Angola, the Congo, Liberia and Sierra Leone.

As is the case with tea, the origin of coffee-drinking is entirely obscure. The first record of its use in Abyssinia dates back to the fifteenth century and it was then said to have been in use since time immemorial, but strangely enough neighboring countries seem to have been quite unaware of its existence. Coffee is as closely associated with

Islam as tea is with China. It is said that it was first used to keep the devout awake during very prolonged religious services. This stirred up a violent opposition from the priests and induced them to declare that coffee was an intoxicating beverage and therefore forbidden by the Koran and severe penalties were threatened to those who became addicted to its use. But, as so often happens, all the priestly thunder did little to stop the rapid spread of coffee-drinking among Arabian Muslims, in fact, it soon became their national drink.

In the seventeenth century coffee was introduced to Europe from Constantinople via Venice where the first coffee-houses were opened. In London the first coffee-house appeared in 1652, but, as in Arabia, the black drink soon ran into opposition. In England, Charles II tried to suppress the coffee-houses on the ground that they were hot-beds of political agitation, an assumption which in all probability then had—and still has—some justification. In Germany, a special license, difficult to obtain, was required before anyone could legitimately roast a coffee bean.

Until the close of the seventeenth century all coffee came from Yemen where alone the true mocca is still produced; but at about that time plants were introduced to Java and successfully cultivated. The Portuguese brought coffee cultivation to Ceylon and in 1718 Sir Nicholas Lawes, Governor of Jamaica, started its cultivation on the American continent; and there most of the world's supply is now produced.

The wide demand for coffee from which the only physiologically active substance—caffein—has been removed, and the extent to which entirely inactive coffee surrogates—chicory for example—are used, shows how essential a part of Western man's diet coffee drinking has become. He is frightened to use it as the stimulant it is meant to be; and yet he will not do without it. Tea has so far escaped chemical emasculation, though here too such lowly brews as camomile, the flowers of the lime tree, mint, and fennel are widely used.

CHOCOLATE

Cocoa was unknown to the rest of the world before the discovery of America, where it was found in common use and highly esteemed by the Aztecs in Mexico. Their drink was a frothy beverage made of roasted cacao beans finely ground and mixed with peppers and other spices. It was both bitter and pungent, but mildly stimulating as the beans contains 2.2 per cent theobromine and 0.1 per cent caffein. It is also nourishing, owing to its high content of cacao butter. The Aztec name for this drink was chocolatl.

The *Conquistadores* improved the drink by adding sugar, which was of course unknown to the Aztecs, and they guarded their secret for nearly a century. It then became known in Italy, Germany, and France; and in 1657, a Frenchman opened a shop in London where he sold solid chocolate for making the beverage at 15 shillings per pound. Soon fashionable chocolate houses were established for the rich in most European capitals and in the year 1700 the English had the bright idea of adding milk and so making milk chocolate. From then on the drinking of cocoa, made from prepared powder, suffered a gradual decline, while the abolition of high import duties and the rising supply brought down the price and led to the now almost universal consumption of chocolate in the solid form.

The cacao tree will only grow within 20 degrees north and 20 south of the equator. It requires very good deep soil, protection against wind, and an evenly distributed rainfall of 50 to 150 inches a year. In spite of these stringent requirements, it is now grown successfully in tropical West Africa, Brazil, Venezuela, Ecuador, Ceylon, Java, and a few other countries. The tree is very striking, growing huge pods directly out of the trunk and the main branches.

In Africa, the transport of these heavy pods encountered great difficulties, owing to the harassment of man and beast by the tsetse fly which spread the dreaded sleeping-sickness and made the keeping of pack animals impossible in the hot rain forests where alone cacao will grow. So it happened that the cultivation of cacao was chiefly responsible for the building of a least 500 miles of railroads and 3000 miles of good roads suitable for motorized transport. The absence of good harbors and the thundering Atlantic surf on the west coast of Africa were other serious impediments to the loading of the precious cargo. The boats had to anchor far out at sea and were served by small and dangerous surf-riding boats that frequently capsized in the heavy breakers. This difficulty was also overcome by the construction of deep-sea harbors, and thus an Aztec discovery greatly helped the advancement of West Africa hundreds of years after the inventors had been ruthlessly exterminated.

I have picked out only a few items which may interest the reader and will not attempt to cover the immense field of the prehistorical and historical discoveries of what modern man eats—the spices, fruits, vegetables, bakery, oils, cheeses, etc., nor the manifold methods of food conservation, as that would take us too far afield. We shall rather, in the next chapter, deal with some of modern man's problems and achievements in matters of feeding and then in the final chapter indulge in a little speculation upon what the future may have in store.

SEVEN

Modern Man and His Food

THE SWEAT OF HIS FACE

The ancient Biblical curse "in the sweat of thy face shalt thou eat bread" with which Adam was driven out of the Garden of Eden still rests heavily upon affluent modern man. His machines have relieved him to a great extent of the sweat of toiling with his hands; he now suffers from the sweat of fear. We are not here concerned with his fear of nuclear weapons, nor with the dread of hunger which still holds hundreds of millions of our fellow men in its terrifying grip; of this latter fear we shall have more to say in another context. Here we shall speak only of the appalling myths which modern man is weaving around almost everything he eats.

Not so long ago it was grandmother who spun such myths, but as grandmother's authority was limited and each grandmother had myths of her own, they were not taken too seriously and no harm was done. But today the scientists have taken over from the grandmothers and are backed by undisputed authority in spite of the fact that—in medicine at least—much of their time is spent in proving each other wrong.

Scientists, and the lay world they have set themselves up to tutor, have implicit faith in the statistical analysis of small numbers, the comportment of small laboratory animals, and the behavior of the contents of small laboratory glassware. In the biochemical field, things like psychology, history, paleontology, and the study of behavior are considered not quite "exact" science, because they cannot to the same extent be subjected to standard procedures of experimentation. Somehow the great amount of patient research that is being conducted in these fields is less likely to be noised abroad.

The result is that—not miserable enough with bombs, poverty, and overpopulation—the wretched health-conscious citizen is being hounded by a rapid succession of food scares. In the long run, sound common sense and what little remains of our feeding instincts usually prevail over scientific hyperboles, which then quietly sink into oblivion. But unfortunately, before they fizzle out, up come scientific Cassandras with new scares hailed as scientific discoveries. Through the years we have witnessed salt scares, pepper scares, meat scares, egg scares, and even milk has come under grave suspicion.

The upper nutritional echelons are just emerging out of the battle of the fatty acids—saturated versus unsaturated—in which the control of blood cholesterol was the contention and saving mankind from its arteries the prize. Obviously when the body is given no suitable material out of which to manufacture cholesterol, the blood level goes down; but that has in no way influenced the factors that made it rise in the first instance and these are just the factors that urgently require investigating. The upshot is that food, abnormally high blood cholesterol levels, and vascular disease are after all not causally related, so that we may safely return to the delicious fresh butter and the eggs and bacon of our benighted forefathers, instead of hopefully drinking rather disgusting polyunsaturated oils. This maturer insight into the matter is rather shamefacedly hidden away in abstruse scientific papers, where it is unlikely to catch the roving eye of copy-happy journalists, among whom recantations of earlier enthusiasms are particularly unwelcome. Thus many an apprehensive feeder is still eating an egg with emotions that range from cussed bravura over trepidation to mortal terror, instead of merely enjoying its palatability.

But hardly are those in the know beginning to breathe more freely, when the all too credulous are cast back into jitters. One eminent scientist finds that coronary thrombosis lurks in the sugar with which you sweeten your tea and sour jam. If this notion had remained a suggestion whispered in the inner circle of interested scientists who could then have gone to work quietly, no harm would have been done. Alas, it was published in one of the best and world-widely read medical journals which is traditionally scanned every week by science reporters in search of sensational discoveries of general interest. So while the unsaturated fats are still in the fire, sugar has become the latest suspect. Though the professor's facts, figures, and interpretations are being severely taken to task by his fellow scientists, we will soon be in the throes of a sugar crisis and, for all we know, the market may slump while saccharin triumphantly booms.

Not enough with this blow to our sweet tooth, another researcher has isolated a substance—which will produce cancer when rubbed into the skin of a rabbit—from meat barbecued over an open wood-fire. Thus another innocent

Sunday pleasure threatens to go up in an ugly, fear-spelling cloud of smoke.

To a detached observer it looks as if everybody is struggling frantically to put more and more food-fears into people's heads and to spoil what should be pride in man's incredible nutritional achievements and the pleasures he derives from them. Of course this is not really so; it is all done in good faith, if a little rashly. The real root of the trouble is that modern man has become alarmingly subject to a number of fatal diseases the true causes of which are still utterly baffling to our researchers. Diabetes, obesity, peptic ulcers, high blood-pressure, strokes, rheumatism and coronary thrombosis are but a few examples of such disorders. They are unknown in wild animals and cannot, therefore, be fully elucidated by animal experiments.

With regard to these diseases we are in much the same quandary as was medieval man, desperately trying to find the cause of the black death, or plague. Before the discovery of the microscope and bacteria, this was obviously a futile enterprise; and so he too invented myths in which people believed, putting themselves to endless prophylactic troubles in vain. When a disease is not understood, theories and superstitions necessarily abound and many modern ones are no less odd than the charms, the sacrifices, and the propitiatory rites of old. We know that neither bacteria nor viruses; neither comets nor eclipses; nor the wrath of God are causing modern man's circulatory, metabolic and digestive afflictions. So our laboratory-conditioned researchers go to work on all that seems left to them: man's food, drink, and smoke. With what amounts to blind conservatism, traditionalism and almost obstinacy, they persist in ignoring one field in which there is at least a very good chance of finding the real answers to these problems and that lies in the working of the human brain, fiercely battling with all the fears, anxieties and conflicts which the onrush of civilization has created.

The human mind cannot be measured, it cannot be reproduced in laboratory animals; nor can it, as yet, be chemically or physically analyzed. To the average laboratory worker, and it is he who has the last word in current medical thinking, dealing with the mind appears, to use Felix Timmerman's rude simile, like trying to keep a flatus in a birdcage. The laboratory-conditioned medical researcher eschews with horror the suggestion that the working of the brain might be a determining factor in his investigations. He sees the mind as not being amenable to *scientific* research, as he interprets the term. He is, therefore, forced to pretend that it has no bearing on his work, though he does, almost reluctantly, admit that it exists.

Modern man will still for some time continue to be hounded by fears of what he eats; whereby these largely unfounded dreads create just the emotional conditions favorable to the insurgence of those many disorders in which the working of the brain may well play by far the most important role.

Food Fads and Fancies

Every day we hear people say that such-and-such food does not agree with them, that they cannot digest it, that their stomach revolts, etc. It is true that our stomach is a marvelously intricate, though very robust, organ and that food allergies to one particular item, though rare, do exist; but it is not true that the stomach has a brain of its own which alone would enable it to make fine distinctions about what goes into it. The only brain that can do this is in our head where it is served by the senses. The stomach is a very muscular sac with a lining that secretes extremely potent digestive chemicals and enzymes. Its mechanical and secretory function may to some extent be increased or decreased by the greater or lesser local stimulus of various foods, but these functions are to a far greater degree subject to what the brain thinks about what is being eaten. If a person likes highly spiced foods and is not afraid to eat them, he will digest them perfectly; yet if he eats semolina pudding with loathing, it will lie heavily and uncomfortably in his stomach. Another person who has been brought up to believe that milk rice is good for him, will digest it with ease and may even relish it, while a goulash, well-seasoned with paprika, which he believes to be indigestible, will keep him awake most of the night. The stomachs of these two people can be identical in all respects; their varying reactions are entirely due to their different attitudes towards food.

Rather than thinking of the stomach as a highly discriminating sense organ such as are our eyes, our taste, smell and the sense of touch in the mouth, we should think of it rather like a washing machine. In most cases, saying that it can digest some things and not others is like contending that an automatic laundry machine will wash perfectly bedsheets, tablecloths, and shirts, but not socks. The nature of the food eaten cannot influence the process of digestion to anything like the extent to which the brain's fears, fads, and fancies can. Banal indigestion is rarely caused by what is eaten, but rather by the eater's emotional attitude to what he has eaten or the emotional tension under which he ate.

When this is explained to a sceptical patient, he almost invariably smiles triumphantly and says: "Ah! But I have experimented and I can assure you that every time I eat raw tomatoes," or whatever it may be, "I get this awful indigestion, so there really can be no doubt that the raw tomatoes do cause it, particularly as boiled or fried tomatoes never give me indigestion." Or, as one often hears: "Yes, I can eat ham, but pork is like poison." Or again: "I cannot digest whipped cream." Doctor's question: "Well, what about milk and butter?" Patient's answer: "Oh yes, those I can digest perfectly." These "experiments" are of the same ilk as many performed in our laboratories with the most meticulous care. The facts are beyond dispute. The tomatoes, the pork and the whipped cream are real; and very real too is the indigestion following their consumption; and yet there must be a snag somewhere hidden by a short-circuit in the causative reasoning on the phenomenon.

The real sequence of events that has led to all the trouble is as follows: One day the patient had indigestion because he was under some emotional strain. It is in the nature of the human mind that it will never blame itself, but must of needs find a scapegoat for any discomfort it causes the body. In our first case the patient picked on the innocent tomatoes he happened to have eaten at his last meal. Having squarely and satisfactorily placed the blame on the tomatoes, this happy conviction soon relieves the indigestion, particularly because it is so easy to avoid a recurrence by avoiding raw tomatoes and it is there and then resolved to do just that. But after a while the sight of a luscious tomato salad causes the resolve to weaken. He says to himself: "Perhaps it wasn't the tomatoes after all; I think I'll risk it, just to make sure." With fear and apprehension the delicious salad is heroically eaten, and half an hour later the patient is burping, feels bloated and has a pain in the pit of his stomach, just in that region known as the hypochondrium (meaning below the rib-cage)

"Aha!" concludes the patient, "So it was the tomatoes after all." Henceforth the resolve never to touch another raw tomato becomes a vow. As fear, and perhaps fear alone, abruptly stops the flow of gastric juices, it is easy to prove to the patient that this, and not the tomato, is the cause of his indigestion; for if he is given a liberal quantity of dilute hydrochloric acid to sip during his meal, he can eat all the tomatoes he wants without a twinge. The same reasoning applies to the pork, the whipped cream, and the hundreds of other items of diet which nervous patients are so very apt to keep under suspicion.

It follows that modern man should develop more confidence in the digestive powers of his stomach and be more sceptical of his brain's interpretation of physiological processes. He must learn to stop his brain meddling with these automatic mechanisms over which it has only a negative control, in the sense that fear and apprehensiveness grossly interfere with the normal functioning of a perfectly healthy organ. Unless chemically or bacterially contaminated, no ordinary foods produce either diarrhea or constipation, bloating, or indigestion in an otherwise healthy person, whereas the brain can do all those things. It is about time that these mechanisms should be more generally understood.

VITAMINS

The discovery of vitamins is one of the epoch-making events in the history of the science of nutrition. Any doctor who has worked in those parts of the world where malnutrition and avitaminoses abound, can never get over the intense feeling of gratitude and admiration for the brilliant men who discovered them. The judicious use of vitamins produces results that are quite as quick, dramatic, and often life-saving as any "wonder drug." But when, then, a doctor returns from working among undernourished people into an affluent world where he finds no trace of the avitaminotic ravages he has become accustomed to see and heal, he discovers that all and sundry are guzzling his precious vitamins. He is appalled by this waste of a marvelous and expensive food supplement, and wistfully thinks how much suffering could be relieved if these millions of vitamin pills were available to those who desperately need them.

In the modern Western world only food cranks, alcoholics, or those suffering from debilitating diseases need supplementary vitamins. Even pregnant women—and infants who are healthy, fed normally and freely, and who get plenty of sunshine on their bodies—do wonderfully well without additional vitamins. But in most civilized countries vitamins have become a profitable ramp from which in the majority of cases only the pharmaceutical industry benefits. Vitamins also admirably serve the purpose of the overworked medical practitioner who must somehow disengage himself from time-consuming hypochondriacs. It has been said, probably with some justification, that the richest source of vitamins in the world are the sewers of New York.

OBESITY

One of civilized man's major nutritional problems is obesity, and its importance as a public health concern is almost equal to that of malnutrition in other parts of the world. But there is this difference: We know enough about the essentials of feeding to be able to avoid malnutrition completely; it is no longer a scientific, but rather an economic, educational, and organizational problem. Obesity, on the other hand, is still a hotly discussed medical conundrum.

As was the case with diabetes before the discovery of insulin, theories, therapies, and fads are legion; and this is always a sure sign of our ignorance. In the case of diabetes, all these wild speculations vanished as soon as the true cause of the disease was discovered. Before that great moment in the history of medicine, it was believed that eating too much sugar and starch caused the disease and that it could be cured by eating less. We now know that neither of these assumptions is correct. With regards to obesity we are as yet in this early phase of groping. It is still widely held that the disorder is brought on merely by overeating and that it can be cured by eating less. However, it is beginning to be realized that this is certainly not so, but that some very definite, as yet unknown metabolic abnormality—which may well be hereditary—is at the root of the disorder.

This has nothing to do with the need of the diabetic to control his carbohydrate intake in order to keep his abnormal blood-sugar down nor with the need of the obese to control his caloric intake (even though this does not radically cure the condition and only enables the patient to maintain the status quo). However, some progress in the management of obesity is being made. It has been found that a substance produced in the placenta, known as human chorionic gonadotrophin (HCG), has the property of making abnormal, and only abnormal, fat available to the body for metabolic purposes; thus patients suffering from obesity can utilize this fat instead of food, and are able to live comfortably and go about their usual occupations, eating only 500 calories per day for several weeks, and losing an average of almost a pound per day without any unpleasant side effects. Moreover, after such treatment the patients can eat far more than they could before without regaining any weight, from which it seems to follow that HCG not only enables the patient to reduce weight, but does actually correct the underlying metabolic disorder whatever that may be.

When a patient tries to reduce by merely restricting his caloric intake, the first fats to go are the body's normal deposits which it needs to function properly while the abnormal deposits remain largely untouched. The patients soon begin to look haggard, feel weak, and are often tortured by hunger. This never happens when HCG is combined with the restricted diet. When an obese patient follows a crash diet, all those many secondary clinical conditions which are so frequently associated with obesity —be they circulatory, glandular, arthritic, etc.—tend to get worse, while under treatment with HCG they invariably improve dramatically.

We do not know exactly how HCG brings about this effect, because we still know so little about obesity; but the clinical evidence obtained from tens of thousands of cases shows that the average loss is the same in all forms of obesity, be they mild or severe, in both sexes and at all ages, provided, of course, that all details of the technique are scrupulously followed and that the patient is cooperative. This new method is still frowned upon in some quarters, because we cannot fully explain its mechanism; this is partly because the effect cannot be studied in laboratory animals who do not have the hereditary factor which is responsible for human obesity; partly because no animal, with the single exception of the anthropoid apes produces the human type of chorionic gonadotrophin; and partly because no biochemical tests with which the action of HCG in man can be demonstrated are as yet available. As we have seen, things that cannot be shown to take place in a test tube or in the gizzards of guinea pigs are considered tantamount to quackery. However, the clinical facts are indisputable, nor have they ever been denied by any student who has adhered strictly to the letter of the technique, and so for the present we shall have to content ourselves with an empirical approach which works and wait until experimental research catches up and gives us a more exact interpretation of the mechanisms involved, particularly as the results obtained with HCG are far superior to anything hitherto achieved in this field.

THE POPULATION BOMB

In human beings we are for the first time witnessing an explosive overpopulation which is threatening to outrun the world's food supply. Biologically this phenomenon is unique in two respects. First, that it is worldwide and not particularly localized in a few areas. Secondly, man is the only animal in existence that does not limit its numbers strictly in accordance with available space and food. Extraordinary as it may seem, the view has been advanced that it would be contrary to "the laws of nature" to limit our progeny. Of course the exact opposite is true, and it is entirely contrary to nature not to do so. There is not a single species in the whole animal or vegetable kingdom that does not practice population control and perfectly adjusts its numbers to available resources.

It is now known that this is not due to passive mechanisms such as starvation, disease, parasites, predators, accidents, etc. The delicate balance is actively maintained by each species adopting measures which forestall overpopulation. In animals, including man, the sex drive and capacity enormously exceed the requirements of propagation. In a normally fertile human couple one intercourse a year would be sufficient to keep up a steady annual reproductivity, but that this is neither normal nor compatible with the normal endocrine and gonadal physiology is too obvious to require elaboration. Moreover, it should always be remembered that the causal connection between sex and reproduction is a late Neolithic human discovery. This discovery was an outcome of the culture which the human brain slowly evolved and has as little to do with the laws of nature as shaving and wearing clothes.

Let us for a moment return to the animals where populations are kept extraordinarily constant and see how this is achieved. Except for quite unusual ecological upheavals, wholesale death from starvation is hardly known among wild animals. Predators can only play a minor role among those species that are particularly prone to their inroads; other species not so exposed—especially the predators themselves—practice rigorous birth control. This has been proved beyond doubt among lions, eagles, seals, the arctic skua, and many other species. It is true that epidemics and parasites may occasionally decimate an animal population, but such catastrophes do not occur regularly every year, whereas all those various mechanisms

which keep the population at an optimal density go into
operation at every mating season.

In a given area all the individuals of a species cooperate
in putting these mechanisms into effect and this cooperation is the earliest and most primitive form of social
organization. It is the beginning of all more complex
forms of social structure such as the swarm, the herd, the
colony, etc., including early man's clans, groups, and
tribes. Modern man, however, forgot the original significance of such cooperation for the social welfare of the
species after he learned—only about 8–10,000 years ago
—to control his food supply in some measure. This was
without serious consequences as long as: the world was
thinly populated and there remained vast tracts of land to
be opened up and cultivated; as long as millions of women
died of childbirth; the infant mortality was 30–40 per cent;
the average expectation of life 25 years; murderous warfare
was rife; and lethal epidemics continued to sweep over the
earth in rapid succession. That is how nature works, and if
man with his science interferes with this balance by suc-
ceeding to banish these atrocious calamities, it is surely his
bounden duty to correct the equally catastrophic results of
his interference.

Once upon a time, sex taboos that were strictly observed—abortion, infanticide, head-hunting, and above all
cannibalism—were man's chief methods of active birth
control. The finer cultural evolution of his brain, which
produced moral and ethical values, led him to regard the
suffering these methods entail as unacceptable and so he
had to find new ways to correct the unforeseen emergency
into which his cleverness had cast him. There are many
ways in which animals achieve active birth control. Under
the threat of overpopulation, many female animals are
able to reduce their rate of ovulation, so that in spite of
frequent mounting by the males, they do not conceive.

This is brought about by a slight change in the hormonal balance that controls ovulation, presumably an increase in the secretion of the corpus luteum stimulating hormone from the anterior lobe of the pituitary gland under the influence of some sort of stress. We know also that some animals such as rabbits, foxes, and deer can under environmental stress completely re-absorb fetuses already growing in the uterus.

Among animals the most important and most commonly operative factor in controlling the birth rate is the powerful territorial instinct. It has been studied among animals of all orders, but most extensively among birds. Before the mating season begins the males stake out a territory sufficient to maintain themselves and the prospective family. The size of the territory is exactly in accordance with the amount of food it is able to furnish. The males announce their claim either by song, or a display of plumage, or both. This performance is primarily addressed to the other males of the species and is not, as was so long and so romantically believed, enacted to woo a female. In many species it starts long before the females arrive, but when they do, it indicates to them which male is master of his territory and unless he is that, she will pay no attention to him. These territorial concerts take place at dusk and dawn and their volume gives the local population a clear indication of its density. Strangely enough, late-arriving males, even if they are stronger than the incumbent, are utterly unable to penetrate an established territory. They become outcasts, never find a mate and usually die in isolation. The very sharply defined boundary of a territory is contiguous with several others and there is no room left between them into which a latecomer could squeeze. Instinct seems to drive all the males of a species only towards the colony. The ones that are left out are incapable of founding a new colony at some distance; or they are, as in the case of the skua, actively prevented from doing so. Quite similar behavior has been observed in howler monkeys, fishes, and many other species.

Another widespread method of birth control in the animal world is the hierarchy established by old polygamous males who strictly control the number of younger males that are allowed access to the females, condemning any surplus to absolute celibacy. This has nothing whatever to do with rivalry or jealously; its severity is determined only by the exigencies of population control. This method is common among monkeys that live in troops, such as the baboons, but it is also found in many other gregarious species such as deer, antelopes, and gazelles. There are innumerable variations and elaborations of these natural methods of birth control, but what interests us here is that man, having by his culture lost his natural control, must now find ways and means of re-establishing it.

Paradoxical as it may seem, malnutrition, which is almost non-existent among animals, tends to increase human fertility. It is an old observation that the poor have more children than the rich and for this specious reasons have been adduced, such as that they have nothing better to do in their spare time than to procreate. It is only recently that this phenomenon has found a scientific explanation. The human sex glands produce far more sex hormones than are required for a normal sex urge, the regular rhythm of the menstrual cycle, and the regulation of pregnancy and lactation. Under normal conditions, a substantial part of this surplus is used up in the liver for the synthesis of certain essential amino acids into molecules of human protein. But the liver can only perform this function if it is well stocked with certain factors of the vitamin B complex and provided it is adequately furnished by these essential amino acids coming in from the intestinal tract. The diet of indigent populations, living mostly on oils, carbohydrates, fruit, and vegetables, is particularly liable to be deficient in just these factors with the result that the level of circulating sex hormone is abnormally high, causing excessive libido and increased fertility.

This important cause of overpopulation can be eliminated by providing all women of childbearing age with an adequate supply of the vitamin B complex and proteins rich in essential amino acids, that is, protein of animal origin. If these nutritional items, which can be produced and manufactured in large quantities at a relatively low cost, were to be diverted to this purpose instead of being wasted—as is now the case with fashionable vitamin B and millions of pounds of food made up in the form of slimming powders—this would go a long way to reduce excessive fertility among those who can ill-afford to have large families.

Under normal conditions, a woman who is breast-feeding an infant does not conceive, but among under-nourished or inadequately fed women this is not the case. In the East, I have often heard women say that they continue to breast-feed their infants as long as possible in the hope of warding off yet another pregnancy. Unfortunately this hope is rarely fulfilled and it is nothing uncommon to see women in the later stages of pregnancy suckling an infant that is not yet one year old. That this happens is due to the excess of sex hormones resulting from malnutrition and it can be corrected by better feeding. Nutritional factors also account for the observation that workers of peasant stock tend to have less children when they take up industrial labor, for though they may suffer in general health owing to the monotony of their diet, they are more likely to eat those foods which control an excess of sex hormones. However, dietary measures will, in the present population explosion, hardly be enough to tide us over until science makes the vast strides necessary to raise the food supply sufficiently to catch up with our numbers. Active measures of birth control will have to be resorted to.

We are at last, and often painfully, emerging out of the curious ecclesiastical notion that sex indulged in for the pleasure of instinct gratification is sinful. Among scientists it is now almost generally recognized that the unphysiological and unnatural suppression of the sex urge by exercising abstinence may have mystic, ascetic merits, but that it is quite useless to consider it a workable method of population control. It is simply untrue that for persons who have neither the means, the education, nor the psychological drive to sublimate their libido, prolonged periods of forced abstinence are psychologically or physiologically harmless or even beneficial.

On the other hand, most mechanical and anticonceptional devices, coitus interruptus, and the observation of the "safe" period are neither safe nor esthetically acceptable; they destroy the instinctive spontaneity which is an important part of the enjoyment of sex. This is now generally recognized and scientists all over the world are working hard to find better and more acceptable methods. As cannibalism and infanticide irrevocably belong to a cruder human past, free legalized abortion has been advocated. That the performance of an abortion is wicked and violates the laws of God, man, and nature is upheld only by those who consider it right and just that a "sinner" should suffer years of anguish and heartbreak for a moment of delirious happiness in yielding to the highest imperative in nature which is to multiply, who believe that God is pleased when yet another mouth is added to a hovel full of hungry, screaming brats, and that the victim of rape should suffer for her attacker's brutality.

Yet from many other points of view artificially induced abortion is far from being a civilized solution of the problem. In unskilled hands it is a dangerous procedure and its emotional impact upon the mother is probably greater than that of institutionalized infanticide, where the decision was not of her own making. The mechanical destruction of a living child growing in its mother's womb is utterly repugnant to our whole attitude to life, and ethically tolerable only as a means to avoid still greater suffering, just as the brutality of major surgery is tolerable only for that reason.

In all the animal world it is the female who decides when she is willing and ready to have offspring; rape or coercion are non-existent. Only man, who prides himself in being far superior to the animals, has taken this decision out of the hands of his females. In Paleolithic times when the causal connection between sex and pregnancy was unknown, he and she could indulge their senses freely. But as man was then almost purely carnivorous, excessive fertility was no problem, particularly as crude means of limiting the number of offspring could be resorted to without the least scruple or inhibition. Post-Neolithic man's superior ethics and superior knowledge have rendered cohabitation always subject to the threat of unwanted or unjustified pregnancy. If men and women want to enjoy sex, the decision whether this should or should not result in pregnancy must be returned to the female of the species, as is normal, natural, and ethical.

The question that faced the scientists was, therefore, to find a perfect method of birth control to be given into the hands of the woman. It had to fulfill the following conditions:

1) It must be perfectly harmless and in no way interfere with the menstrual cycle or other functions of the body.

2) It must be 100 per cent sure and reliable.

3) As soon as its use is stopped, normal fertility must be restored at once.

4) During the period of desired sterility, its action must be constant and entirely independent of the time of intercourse.

5) It must prevent either the ripening or the fertilization of the egg cell, so that no new life is formed, even in its earliest stages.

6) It must be esthetically acceptable.

7) It must impose no restriction on either male or female partner.

Until quite recently some of these conditions presented seemingly insurmountable difficulties and then, just as the population problem began to loom as a terrifying prospect, man's ingenuity came up with two perfect answers. One was *The Pill* and the other was an intrauterine device. *The Pill* is already universally known and used, except among orthodox Catholics and persons too poor to afford it. It fulfills all the above requirements, and I need not here go into its perfectly physiological mode of action. However, it still has two disadvantages for the poor and often illiterate millions who need it most. The one is that it is as yet far too expensive; the other, that it requires a moment's daily attention, so that it is not forgotten, and a minimum of reckoning to find the days during which it is suspended. Carelessness in these respects is dangerous, because after it has been taken for some time, pregnancy is very liable to occur if the pill is not taken for a few days. Such things are difficult to impress upon utterly ignorant and wildly superstitious populations.

The intrauterine device does not have these disadvantages. It is a tiny, very cheap plastic appliance which is inserted into the womb and stays there only to be withdrawn when pregnancy is desired. Insertion and withdrawal must be skillfully done, but any midwife or nurse can easily be taught the technique. Though now highly refined and scientifically studied in all its aspects, the method is actually quite old. Arabian camel drivers know that by inserting a small pebble into the uterus of their she-camels they can prevent pregnancy, even if they allow her to be mounted when she comes in heat. Girls working in rubber plantations use a small piece of latex in the same manner. Apart from the need for skillful insertion, the intrauterine device complies with all the criteria for an ideal contraceptive and it is being widely distributed by some governments that are wisely aware of their population problem.

It thus seems as if man has at long last paid about 10,000 years of penalty for having pried into one of nature's most closely guarded secrets when he ate the fruit of the forbidden tree of knowledge in the Garden of Eden.

The Future of Human Feeding

PROPHESYING may be based on a claim to extra-sensory perception, or it may be based on the further spinning of threads which are already on the spindle. It is this second kind of prophecy with which we are here concerned. At any moment unforeseeable discoveries may, and probably will, start entirely new trends, rendering many old ones obsolete. These are the domain of seers and not of speculating scientists.

Man: A Defaulting Mammal

The time is perhaps not too distant when taxonomists will feel tempted to remove man from the Class of Mammals and to give him a class of his own as the only animal which rears its young on the contents of a tin. We now have countless families in which three consecutive generations have been reared without their mother's breast, and there is not a scrap of scientific evidence to suggest that this has harmed either mother or her infant, provided that the directions on the tin are strictly followed. So highly perfected is the science of preparing infant foods and of infant management that artificial feeding is a better safeguard against malnutrition than breast-feeding with its many hazards.

This new trend has been, as new trends always are, strongly opposed from many quarters and this has in the past generated feelings of guilt, envy, and inferiority in mothers who were for many possible reasons unwilling or unable to fulfill their mammalian function. Happily among our young mothers this self-torturing attitude is waning fast. Before science and industry had combined to cater for the newborn, there were only two alternatives: fresh cow's or goat's milk, boiled, and watered down; or the wet nurse (what an awful expression, by the way). The former was nutritionally quite inadequate and the latter a privilege of the rich. Both are rapidly becoming relics of an ugly past.

In the human species the female breast seems to be changing from an organ which exclusively served the rearing of the young into an attribute of sexual attraction and will soon be displayed with the same nonchalance as are today a well-turned pair of female legs. As the breast was never intended to be an object of sexual allure, this is an evolutionary novelty to which no animal has as yet aspired; though in the animal world there are countless examples of organs having assumed functions for which they were never intended.

THE MECHANIZATION OF FOOD PRODUCTION

Originally farmers raised crops and reared domestic animals to feed their families; but then arable land, herds, and flocks became objects of barter, especially in marriages. As civilization increased the number of nonproducers, the farmers began to sell their surpluses and in turn to buy cultural and technical goods, which they themselves were unable to manufacture. Only at a much later stage did farmers produce primarily for the market, specialize in only a few items for which their land was particularly suited, and pay for most of their own food in cash.

On a world scale this development has hitherto been slow and sketchy, often confined to the vicinity of towns. But within the last century the pace of specialization has quickened fantastically due to the narrowing mesh of transport facilities, of roads, railways, ships, and aircraft spreading their network over the globe. Hand-in-hand with this development, the mechanization of farming has led to less men being able to till vaster tracts of land, to control larger herds, and to milk more cows than ever before. The mechanization—and we shall soon be able to say automation—of agriculture and animal husbandry will continue to make spectacular progress, both as regards the intensity of production and universal application, until large scale food production becomes wholly industrialized. The still very young science of pest control can be expected to evolve highly effective and specific insecticides and fungicides, innocuous to man and higher animals, acting through antibiotic rather than toxic mechanisms.

The domestic kitchen is rapidly being replaced by the industrial kitchen. The modern urban, working housewife who has never really learned to cook and has no time to indulge in what is almost becoming a hobby, needs only a small range with an oven, a kettle, a saucepan, and a frying pan to serve meals of an excellence and variety hardly known in the banqueting halls of but a century ago. However, we have not yet quite overcome our industrial resentment. People who pride themselves on their gustatory acumen still claim that a barnyard hen tastes better than a scientifically, industrially raised battery bird; that "fresh" vegetables, having suffered hours, and maybe days, of transport and exposure in an open market, taste better or are more nutritious than tinned or deep-frozen vegetables, grown under optimal conditions, selected for quality and processed almost within minutes of picking. Time and again gourmets have been confounded when asked to distinguish between dishes prepared from "fresh" and preserved foods. Such contests usually end by the preserved food being preferred.

One would think that it is obvious that the collaboration of highly trained agriculturists, professional chefs and specialized engineers can produce better food than the average dilettante housewife, and yet it is still an advertising gimmick to say that the product of such eminently qualified teamwork tastes "just like what Grandma used to make." Obviously also nothing is easier than to emulate any Grandma on an industrial scale. This sentimental hankering for Grandma's special culinary exploits will vanish with the generation in which these are still childhood memories. It is now only a matter of a few years before this comes about, as most modern grandmothers have always been valiant wielders of the can opener.

The busy housewife skillfully steers her shopping-cart through the aisles of the supermarket and deftly picks from the cornucopia stacked to the right and to the left of her. Her mind is fully engaged in maintaining the delicate balance of bellies and budgets, of palates and parsimony. Her problem is no longer to search for what she needs, but rather to resist buying what she does not need. To her all this is little more than just one of the day's chores, yet should a professor of medieval history or a paleontologist stray absent-mindedly into a modern supermarket, he will realize with a shock that a nutritional revolution has taken place and that the produce of the whole world in food and drink is waiting to be served at every table and that this is a new cultural achievement of no mean order.

How many secret tears and how much brave mastication of kitchen disasters has the ingenious cake mix abolished. Were it not for our exquisite breakfast cereals, we would still be condemned to the consumption of porridge. Without industrialization we could not choose from a hundred varieties of bread and a thousand varieties of cakes, biscuits, chocolates, ice creams and sweets. It is only a few years ago that the first supermarket was opened in the City of Rome; the Romans laughed uproariously and predicted its complete failure; today the city is studded with them. It seems certain that this form of shopping will spread to all parts of the world and that it will be accepted with as little reserve as that with which we expect mail services of incredible complexity, the telephone, television, and satellites to function faultlessly. One can almost hear a polite manager explaining to an irate housewife: "I am terribly sorry, Madam, but we have just sold the last can of seal blubber. The new consignment is already in the customs; you see our Eskimo suppliers are a little unreliable; maybe it's the weather. Please accept our apologies."

The Food Pill

When one talks about the future of human feeding, it is almost inevitable that someone says: "Oh yes! Soon we shall swallow a few pills containing all we need." Now that is one thing which is certainly not in store for us, at least not for a very long time to come. It may be that astronauts will be obliged to keep body and soul together in some such way, but for the earthbound rest of us this would not work, if only because it would be intolerable to the organization of our intestinal tract.

This was clearly demonstrated during the now-subsiding Metrecal craze. Metrecal had its less boosted predecessors, and numerous successors trying to muzzle in on an expensive advertising campaign. Complan was one of the first, seemingly perfect, substitutes for normal food and it is to the credit of its makers that it was advertised only to the medical profession for the sole purpose of which concentrates can be usefully employed, which is to put on weight rather than lose it. By adding such a concentrate of all the essential nutritional factors, easily made palatable, easily swallowed, and easily digested, to the diet of an undernourished patient with a poor appetite, he can rapidly regain a satisfactory nutritional status. For this purpose Complan was in regular use long before someone had the commercially profitable but physiologically nonsensical idea of using such a preparation as a means of losing weight. In their commendable promotional fervor these enthusiasts completely ignored the mechanics of human digestion. They conveniently forgot that the human stomach needs some mechanical, chemical, and sensory stimulation to function normally and that the human colon must have some indigestible bulk and roughage to perform its physiological activities. Finally they overlooked that furnishing an obese body with food easily and rapidly assimilated, instead of with food which is slowly and gradually assimilated, is particularly liable to aggravate, rather than relieve, the metabolic disorder which manifests itself as obesity.

As far as one can foresee, man will continue to be omnivorous. Hand in hand with an improving standard of living, the consumption of animal protein will increase and this will markedly improve the health and longevity of future man. It will to some extent diminish abnormal fertility in those countries that are already suffering the dire consequences of malnutrition combined with overpopulation. With complete control of fertility which is now possible in an ethically acceptable manner, we can for the first time hope that soon universal use will be made of this great cultural achievement. Man can now revert to the natural laws against which he has so long offended by giving the female of the species a decisive voice in the control of her pregnancies and by adjusting his numbers to fit the supply of his food and by food I do not mean a mound of rice, but rather a properly balanced diet of high biological value.

The rapid integration of global economics spells hope that the movement of surplus food to areas of deficiency and want will shake off the shackles of political expediency and become effective with the same impartiality and universally approved generosity with which the Red Cross comes to the aid of humans who have suffered disaster. The good will to do this is present, but there are still endless wrinkles that have to be ironed out. Financial, political, and mutual economic considerations as well as the difficulties of controlling distribution still impede an equitable spread of the earth's yield, but on these wrinkles the iron is already hot and heavy.

If man will control his numbers, the vision of a world with food, health, occupation, and leisure for all is no longer a wild utopian dream. If some stale, medieval, and hopelessly anachronistic prejudices can be overcome, this is a goal to which the road is already discernible, and along this road we can now begin to plod with hearts buoyed by new hopes.

OCEANS, DESERTS, AND HYDROPONICS

Three vast potential sources of more food are waiting to be energetically exploited. A detailed study of marine biology and ecology is only just beginning, but the vigor with which it is being pursued promises spectacular results in the near future. In the ocean man is still on a cultural level comparable to that of a Neolithic hunter. Mussels and some crustaceans are being farmed on a small scale, but while fresh-water fish are extensively bred under controlled conditions, the "domestication" of marine fish is still a dream of farsighted planners. There is no reason to doubt that such dreams will soon come true.

With presently available mechanical aids it is theoretically possible to irrigate and render deserts fertile, but before this can be done on a very large scale, we must await new equipment with which the Atomic Age will certainly furnish us. A number of huge schemes are already on the drawing boards and we need not think of such vast areas as the Sahara, the Sind desert in India, the Gobi desert and

Central Australia to realize what these enormous wastes could produce if they were rendered arable, an undertaking which is now no longer unthinkable.

Hydroponics, or the soil-less growing of plants, seems about to emerge from the experimental stage into an industrially feasible, large-scale enterprise. It can yield far more food per square meter of cultivation than normal growth in soil. The whole process is relatively simple to automate and its complete independence of soil, climate and to some extent season, make it appear to hold great promises for the future.

Before these new sources of food can yield appreciable results, they will require an enormous, concerted effort, comparable only to that now being expended on the conquest of space, but far less than the effort expended in two world wars. Modern man is thus quite capable of performing such prodigious feats, and there can, I think, be no question that sooner or later he will.

Enter the Human Psyche

Few observers of current trends in medicine and human physiology will deny that we seem to be on the verge of a revolution in these fields. Barely a century ago, the old humoral pathology was ousted by Virchow's cellular pathology. At the beginning of the twentieth century, the throne of medical thinking was usurped by bacteriology. Now the heyday of this science is over. Its once tyrannical and fertile vigor is exhausted; it has become old, stagnant, dull, and barren after a brief but spectacular career. But before it sank into senility, it gave birth to the study of viruses. Virology became an exciting and challenging field for a new generation of young and eager researchers. It has not yet fulfilled its mission, but its goals and limitations are becoming clear and the approaches have been planned. Soon it, too, will be conquered territory, and the thrills of victory will subside.

Plaques, pestilences and infections are now largely under control; surgery and midwifery have developed a technical perfection that seems hard to surpass by any great forward leaps; we have such a plethora of diagnostic procedures that our clinical laboratories are happy to furnish us with far more information than we can usefully employ in the treatment of the sick; and the essentials of hygiene and nutrition are known. Yet in spite of all these achievements, the bulk of modern man's ill health still looms threateningly over us. Cancer, rheumatism, peptic ulcers, diabetes, obesity, high blood-pressure, coronary thrombosis, and many other disorders have hardly been touched by all this past researching. Intensive work has been and is still being done in all these fields, but so far we have only been able to alleviate symptoms; about causes little or nothing is known and we are getting a little bored with unconvincing, though sensational, scares that do little more than deprive mankind of yet another pleasure. The question thus arises: What next?

The conviction is gradually—all too gradually—gaining ground that none of these problems can be solved unless the psyche is placed on the vacant throne. In many quarters this seemingly most reasonable suggestion is looked upon with scorn, as if it were a sort of Black Magic; perhaps this is because muddling hopefully along is sometimes preferred to drastic innovations. Our scientific journals are full of very learned and often abstruse bio-chemical research, of inconclusive statistical analyses with never a mention of the psyche which must surely be deeply involved in all things human. Much of modern medical research is conducted as if it were dealing with a decerebrated body and it is this attitude which, I firmly believe, blocks progress in the understanding of many of modern man's ailments.

The introduction of the psyche as something to be reckoned with into the whole field of human pathology opens up vast vistas of progress, renders reams of speculation obsolete, means thinking on a new and entirely different plane and a violent breaking-up of the hardened crusts of scientific conventions. Little wonder then that great efforts are being made to ignore the writing on the wall and to stave off the awful moment. But the crust is wearing thin and is already cracking faster than it can be mended. For those who want to be saved, it is time to get aboard the psychic icebreaker, before they find themselves marooned on the melting floes of purely somatic medicine.

Psychophysiology seems about to burst the bounds of psychiatry and flow invigoratingly over the whole range of medical thinking. When this happens, it will have a profound influence on human nutrition. Many now almost universal complaints such as constipation, many forms of chronic diarrhea and indigestion, the irritable colon, will vanish, because it will at last be understood that they are the result of wrong thinking rather than wrong feeding. With a few exceptions such as obesity and diabetes, a mass of unmotivated, fancy and often fantastic diets will disappear from hospital charts, much to the relief of unnecessarily harassed dieticians. For instance, it has already been proved in a carefully controlled study of a very large number of cases that ulcer patients do just as well on a normal general diet as on the once famous Sippy milk diet. In the shrines of learning some modern stomach specialists can be brought to admit in a hushed whisper that psychic factors "may" play a role in causing ulcers, but a well-founded dread of ridicule usually prevents them from mentioning this awful suspicion in their published treatises.

All this talk about whether this or that "does not agree with me" will cease once it is generally realized that which food does and which food does not agree (sic!) with one depends, with very few exceptions, on one's emotional attitude to such food; it does not depend a whit on stomachic or intestinal idiosyncrasies. In Latin countries, particularly France and Italy, that much maligned organ, the liver, will at last find peace in intelligent neglect. Only a physician who has worked in these countries can appreciate the emotional havoc and the *malades imaginaires* created by this cult of the *foie* or *fegato,* as the case may be. The liver is an extraordinarily hardy and robust organ. It may be damaged by infections, new growths or severe nutritional deficiencies, particularly of proteins and vitamins, but it is never harmed directly by excesses of ordinary food nor even by alcohol as such. As I have already said elsewhere, it is the nutritional deficiency to which alcoholics are prone that causes cirrhosis of the liver. Even in countries with a "liver fixation," the time must surely come when we shall hear less about the woes which patients—and alas, all too often their physicians—still attribute to this relatively inoffensive organ and with that another host of irksome dietary taboos will vanish.

Thus, rather than add new complications to our life, the general acceptance of psycho-physiological mechanisms in the interpretation of most of modern man's ailments will at least lead to a much greater dietary freedom and less food anxiety; though of course it will do much more than that. By their training, scientists are—or should be—an openminded sort of people, and whenever something unusual happens in their laboratories or is discovered at a patient's bedside, the phenomenon is pursued with energy, ingenuity and largely without bias. Yet when such a phenomenon clearly calls for a psychic interpretation, physicians, other than psychiatrists, who unfortunately profess not to deal with bodily suffering, shut their scientific eyes and turn their backs, as if they were frightened to admit the psyche into their pathological reasoning. They will at best prescribe a sedative or a tranquilizer or, as a last resort, hand the case over to a psychiatrist for psychotherapy, though in most cases a matter-of-fact and clearly given interpretation of the psycho-physiological mechanisms involved by the treating physician would be perfectly adequate. It would also save the patient the emotional trauma of being referred to a psychiatrist.

This extraordinary, negative attitude is still so common, that one wonders what the doctors are really frightened of. Perhaps their early training and their later choice of reading has rendered them shy and distrustful of thinking in psycho-physiological terms. Perhaps they fear to lose themselves in what appears to them to be a tangled undergrowth of strange terminology in current psycho-analytical literature; or could it be that the pursuance of such research might all too abruptly bring us up against the need to accept, and hence to explain scientifically, extra-sensory perception. Today very few flatly deny its existence, but fewer still are those who can, with scientific equanimity, consider the upheavals that will ensue when E.S.P. acquires the full scientific dignity and status which the future surely has in store for it.

Pierre Teilhard de Chardin's magnificent vision of the evolutionary unity of body and psyche will for many years to come be the starting point of such advanced research. While Freud will always be remembered as the great physiologist of the human mind, Chardin will turn out to be its Darwin. His notion of the psyche as an entity distinct from the somatic evolution of the human brain and that this entity is subject to an evolutionary process in a cosmic stratum, which Chardin calls the Nöosphere, has all the characteristics of one of those gigantic strides which genius sometimes takes.

A Few References

ARDREY, ROBERT	*African Genesis*	Collins, 1961
	The Territorial Imperative	Collins, 1966
BLISS, EUGENE	*Roots of Behaviour*	New York: Harper & Row, 1962
BODENHEIMER, K.	*Insects as Human Food*	The Hague: Junk, 1951
CARPENTER, C. R.	Studies of a Primate Population (in Roots of Behaviour)	New York: Harper & Row, 1962
CARRINGTON, R.	*Elephants*	Pelican A 539
COLBERT, EDWIN	*Evolution of Vertebrates*	Science Editions, Inc.; 1961
COLE, SONIA	The Neolithic Revolution	British Museum 1959
DART, RAYMOND	"The Relationship of Brain Size and Brain Pattern to Human Status"	*S. African J. Medic. Sciences,* 1956
	"Africa's Place in the Evolution of Man"	*Proc. Ass. Sc; & Tech. Soc. of S. Africa,* 1960
	"Africa's Place in the Emergence of Civilization"	*S. African Broad-casting Corp.*

DESMOND, MORRIS	*The Naked Ape*	Jonathan Cape, 1967
DURANT, WILL	*The Life of Greece*	New York: Simon & Schuster, 1939
FENTO, C. L. & M. A.	*The Fossil Book*	Garden City: Doubleday & Company, Inc.
FISHER, R. A.	*The Genetic Theory of Natural Selection*	Dover Publications
GOODALL, JANE	"My Life among Wild Chimpanzees"	*Nat. Geog. Mag.*, August 1963
HARLAND, BRIAN	"The Great InfraCambrian Ice Age"	*Scientific American,* August 1964
HOGG, GARRY	*Cannibalism and Human Sacrifice*	Pan Books
HOWELLS, WILLIAM	*Ideas on Human Evolution*	Cambridge: Harvard Univ. Press, 1962
HUXLEY, JULIAN	*Evolution in Action*	Pelican A 617
KOHLER, WOLFGANG	*The Mentality of Apes*	Pelican A 382
MACNEISH, R.	"The Origins of New World Civilizations"	*Scientific American,* Nov. 1964
OAKLEY, KENNETH	Man the Toolmaker The Earliest Toolmakers	Brit. Museum, 1958 Contrib. Gottfried Kurt's Evolution and Hominization, Gustav Fischer Verl.
PETTER, J. J.	Recherches sur l'Ecologie et l'Ethologie des Lémurien Malagaches	Muséum National d'Histoire Naturelle Paris, 1962
PIGGOTT, STUART	*Prehistoric India*	Penguin, 1952
REYNOLDS, VERNON	*The Apes*	E. P. Dutton, 1967
ROMER, ALFRED S.	*Man and the Vertebrates*	Pelican A 303 & A 304

RHODES, F. H. T.	*The Evolution of Life*	Pelican A 512
SIMEONS, A. T. W.	*Man's Presumptuous Brain*	London: Longmans & Greene, 1961 Dutton New York
SIMPSON, GAYLORD	*The Meaning of Evolution*	New Haven: Yale Univ. Press, 1949
SMITH, MAYNARD	*The Theory of Evolution*	Pelican A 433
DE CHARDIN, P. T.	*The Phenomenon of Man*	Collins, 1960
	The Future of Man	Collins, 1964
WECKER, STANLEY	"Habitat Selection"	*Scientific American,* Oct. 1964

Index